American Language Hub

LEVEL 4B
Workbook

with Key + access to Audio

macmillan education

Macmillan Education
4 Crinan Street
London N1 9XW
A division of Macmillan Education Limited

Companies and representatives throughout the world

American Language Hub Level 4B Workbook with Key ISBN 978-1-380-04745-8
American Language Hub Level 4B Workbook with Key + access to Audio
ISBN 978-1-380-04739-7

Written by Signature Manuscripts

Signature Manuscripts has asserted their right to be identified as the author of this work in accordance with the Copyright, Designs and Patents Act 1988.

First published 2020

Original design by emc design ltd
Page make-up by SPi Global
Cover design based on original design by Restless
Cover photograph by plainpicture/Westend61/Uwe Umstätter
Picture research by Emily Taylor

The author and publishers would like to thank the following for permission to reproduce their photographs:
Alamy/ClassicStock p71, Alamy/Sean Pavone p60, Alamy/UpperCut Images p55; **Getty Images**/AFP p42, Getty Images/Andresr p66, Getty Images/AzmanL p39, Getty Images/Bettmann p53, Getty Images/Bloomberg p52, Getty Images/Caiaimage p45, Getty Images/Caiaimage/Paul Bradbury p63, Getty Images/Alejandro Camacho Beomont p41, Getty Images/FG Trade p48(bl), Getty Images/Flashpop p70, Getty Images/fStop Images – Halfdark p67, Getty Images/Hoxton p40, Getty Images/Jacobs Stock Photography Ltd p54, Getty Images/Dan Kitwood p50, Getty Images/Yaroslav Kushta p48(tl), Getty Images/Jon Lovette p46(b), Getty Images/Nikada p64, Getty Images/ONOKY - Eric Audras p73, Getty Images/Pekic p68, Getty Images/Jose Luis Pelaez Inc p49, Getty Images/Plume Creative p61, Getty Images/Matthias Ritzmann p58, Getty Images/Shaunl p57, Getty Images/Skynesher p48 (arguing), Getty Images/Donald Iain Smith p72, Getty Images/SolStock p50, Getty Images/Towfiqu Photography p59, Getty Images/Klaus Vedfelt p43, Getty Images/Westend61 p62; **Shutterstock** pp47, 56.

Additional sources: Hannah, S. 2018, *It's no mystery that crime is the biggest-selling genre in books*, Guardian, p58.

Printed and bound in Mexico
by Compañía Editorial Ultra, S.A. de C.V.

2021 2020
04 03 02 01

Contents

6.1 Coming of age

GRAMMAR

Obligation, prohibition and permission

A **Choose the correct options (a, b or c) to complete the sentences.**

1 It's late. We ___ be going because we have an early start tomorrow.

a supposed b should c allowed

2 Don't worry – you're ___ to bring drinks in here.

a allowed b obliged c needed

3 We ___ be home by Tuesday because it's Tom's birthday on Wednesday.

a must not b have to c required

4 US citizens ___ to obtain a visa prior to arrival.

a are needed b should c are not required

5 You ___ join any clubs or societies in college, but it's worth considering.

a have to b should c don't have to

6 Sorry we're late. We were ___ arrive at lunchtime, but the traffic was terrible.

a supposed to b obliged to c allowed to

7 Put that down! You know you're not ___ to play with scissors!

a obliged b allowed c required

8 No offense, but you really don't look well. I think you ___ see someone about that cough.

a should b must c can

B **Complete the second sentence so that it has a similar meaning to the first using the words in bold.**

1 Talking in the library is strictly forbidden.

allowed

You ______________________ in the library.

2 It's a good idea to learn some Portuguese before arriving in Rio.

should

He ______________________ some Portuguese before arriving in Rio.

3 Please allow me to deal with the problem myself.

let

Will you ______________________ the problem myself?

4 Don't you dare tell anyone what I said! It's a secret.

must not

You ______________________ what I said!

5 Is it compulsory to stay here until the end?

obliged

Are ______________________ here until the end?

6 I don't think you need to add more salt to the stir-fry.

have

You ______________________ more salt to the stir-fry.

7 I can't talk now; they told me to study for tomorrow.

supposed

I can't talk now; I ______________________ for tomorrow.

8 You don't have to come to the meeting if you don't want to.

obliged

You ______________________ to come to the meeting if you don't want to.

PRONUNCIATION
Intonation to show interest

6.1 **A Listen to the conversation. What kind of intonation does Tom use in the underlined phrases to show interest: rise, fall or rise-fall?**

Tess: Did you hear about Rob and Maria?

Tom: No …

Tess: Well, they're an item!

Tom: No way. That's amazing!

Tess: I know. They got together at the party last week. It was a little embarrassing though, because Rob's ex-girlfriend was there.

Tom: You're kidding!

Tess: Hashtag *not kidding* …

6.2 **B Listen to the conversations. In which of the responses (1–6) does the speaker use intonation to show interest?**

1 **A:** He was standing on stage ready to give his speech and he just … froze. He couldn't say a word.
B: How embarrassing.

2 **A:** It's the first time that any company has launched a commercial flight into space. I mean, how cool!
B: Interesting.

3 **A:** I can't believe they won't give me a refund because I'd opened the packaging.
B: That's ridiculous.

4 **A:** I can't believe it! We've won! We've won the lottery – look, all six numbers!
B: That's amazing.

5 **A:** The traffic was absolutely terrible, then it started raining. That turned into a hurricane! Then, to top it all off, the car broke down. It was the worst few hours of my life.
B: What a nightmare.

6 **A:** Have you seen the score? The Orlando Lions are leading 4-0!
B: You're joking.

6.3 **C Listen to the interested responses in Exercise B again and repeat.**

VOCABULARY
Education

A Match the beginnings of the sentences (1–6) to the endings (a–f).

1 She goes to a boarding school and ___
2 Subjects like math and history are required ___
3 Not everybody wants to go into higher education ___
4 She went to a very expensive private school ___
5 They lived near a very good public school ___
6 There were some unusual subjects in the curriculum ___

a so they didn't have to pay for their children's education.
b with fees of $36,000 a year.
c which you don't find at many schools.
d until the age of 16 when you can choose what to focus on.
e after they leave high school.
f only sees her family during school holidays.

B Complete the interview with the words in the box.

campus graduate high lectures (x2) seminars scholarship vocational

Presenter: So you famously dropped out of college. Can you tell us a little more about that?

Jo: Yeah, sure. Well, back in the 90s, I was studying for a degree in business management at New York University. I'd actually earned a [1]__________ to study there based on my academic performance in [2]__________ school. My grades meant I could pretty much choose which college to go to, but NYU was the only university that offered to pay for part of my tuition – so they seemed like a good option.

Presenter: Absolutely! NYU is a great university, too. The [3]__________ is right in the heart of Greenwich Village, isn't it?

Jo: Yes, that's right. Every morning, on my way to [4]__________, I'd walk through Washington Square Park and past its famous marble arch … it was definitely an inspiring place to study, that's for sure.

Presenter: Did you enjoy the [5]__________?

Jo: Uh, yes. They were interesting, but actually I found the [6]__________ far more useful. I used to love having in-depth discussions about the details of business management! Sad, I know …

Presenter: Ha ha! Not at all. But, in the end, you didn't actually [7]__________? What happened?

Jo: No, I never finished. In our third year, we had to do a work experience placement. It was a chance to gain some [8]__________ experience and learn about the practical side of managing a firm. I spent three months working under Karen Barton at Barton Technology.

Presenter: Wow, I bet that was a great opportunity.

Jo: Yes, too good in fact. Karen felt I had great potential and offered me a job. That was six years ago and now I'm a partner!

GRAMMAR
Articles

A Choose the correct options to complete the sentences.

1 There are some beautiful islands and beaches in *a* / *the* / – Philippines.
2 I'd say taking the subway would be *a* / *an* / *the* easiest way to get into town.
3 Look over there! There's someone flying *a* / *the* / – drone.
4 Some colleges ask you to attend *a* / *an* / *the* interview before offering you a spot.
5 I think *a* / *the* / – climate change is a bigger problem than most people realize.
6 I think *a* / *the* / – Japanese food is probably the best in the world!
7 Sorry, I'm a little busy. Can you just give me *a* / *the* / – minute?
8 Did you actually do *a* / *the* / – shopping this week? The fridge is empty!

B Complete the sentences with *a*, *an*, *the* or – (no article).

1 The Day of the Dead is __________ interesting tradition which we don't celebrate in __________ US.
2 It's my dream to visit some of the world's best historical sites, like __________ Pyramids of Giza or __________ Stonehenge.
3 Megan visited __________ new local hospital and told me it was __________ best she's ever seen.
4 We were staying in __________ Berlin because I had __________ job interview.
5 I grew up in __________ small town called Telluride near __________ Rocky Mountains.
6 I really love __________ music, but I like __________ sports, too.
7 Sorry, I'm a little lost. Do you know __________ way to __________ train station?
8 We left __________ River Nile and headed toward __________ Sahara Desert.

C Find and correct ten mistakes with articles in the text.

The Bullet Ant Initiation

BY **LUCAS HERNANDEZ**
PUBLISHED OCTOBER 15, 2019

There are many interesting coming-of-age traditions around a world, but few are as scary (or as painful) as the Sateré-Mawé Bullet Ant Initiation.

The Sateré-Mawé tribe live deep in an Amazon rainforest in Brazil. When boys in the tribe turn 13, they are sent into the jungle to search for the specific species of ant – the bullet ant. These ants are known for their particularly strong sting, which can cause the extreme pain for up to 24 hours.

Once the boys find an ants, they put them into a glove with the stingers pointing upward. You might think that just catching this highly venomous insect was enough of a initiation, but that's nothing! Each boy then has to wear glove for ten minutes!

A initiation can last months, with the boys repeatedly wearing the glove – sometimes more than 20 times. Your first reaction when being stung by bullet ant would probably be to scream, but the boys try to keep calm to hide their weakness – enduring pain is part of the transition to the manhood.

PRONUNCIATION
Intrusive /j/ sounds

6.4 **A Listen to the sentences below. Notice the /j/ sound that appears between the words connected with a (‿).**

1 The Sateré-Mawé tribe live deep in the‿Amazon rainforest in Brazil.

2 Once the boys find the‿ants, they put them into a glove with the stingers pointing upward.

3 Your first reaction when being stung by‿a bullet ant would probably be to scream.

6.5 **B Draw a (‿) between any words you think are linked by a /j/ sound. Then listen and check.**

1 The ants have a venomous sting.

2 The age-old tradition of land diving

3 The second Monday of January is a special day in Japan.

4 These young adults then go on to celebrate at parties in the evening.

5 It's a coming-of-age movie about three young friends growing up together.

6 I often wonder what it would be like to be in the Sateré-Mawé tribe and do the initiation!

6.5 **C Listen again and repeat the sentences.**

VOCABULARY
Compound adjectives; Phrases with *make* and *do*

A Complete the sentences with the words in the box. Add hyphens where necessary.

bedroom date fashioned grown known minute risk seeking

1 As a child, he became a well ______________ musician.

2 It's an old ______________ house, but it certainly has great charm.

3 They were making last ______________ plans for their summer vacation.

4 Make sure you have up-to ______________ software to protect your computer from viruses.

5 The plan to go on a thrill ______________ adventure vacation was not met with enthusiasm.

6 It's a high ______________ business, but there are good prospects for promotion.

7 They bought a seven ______________ house in the countryside.

8 She insisted on organically ______________ food and drinks without sugar.

B Rewrite the sentences with an appropriate compound adjective.

1 My commute lasts two hours.
I have a ______________ commute.

2 The journey is about 100 miles.
It's a ______________ journey.

3 Their children generally behave well.
Their children are generally ______________.

4 As a singer, he is famous around the world.
He's a ______________ singer.

5 This movie is terrible! Will it never end?
This movie is ______________!

6 I'd like to visit a country where everyone speaks Spanish.
I'd like to visit a ______________ country.

C Complete the sentences with the correct form of *make* or *do*.

1 You should have ______________ allowances for the fact that he's only 15.

2 ______________ a good impression at an interview starts with looking professional.

3 In the past, people ______________ without a lot of things we take for granted today.

4 It's a difficult situation, but I'm ______________ the best of it.

5 I wonder if you could ______________ me a favor?

6 Leave them alone – they're not ______________ any harm.

7 Everyone said their marriage would fail, but they're ______________ a go of it.

8 I wonder if we will ever ______________ away with cell phones. Maybe we'll invent something better!

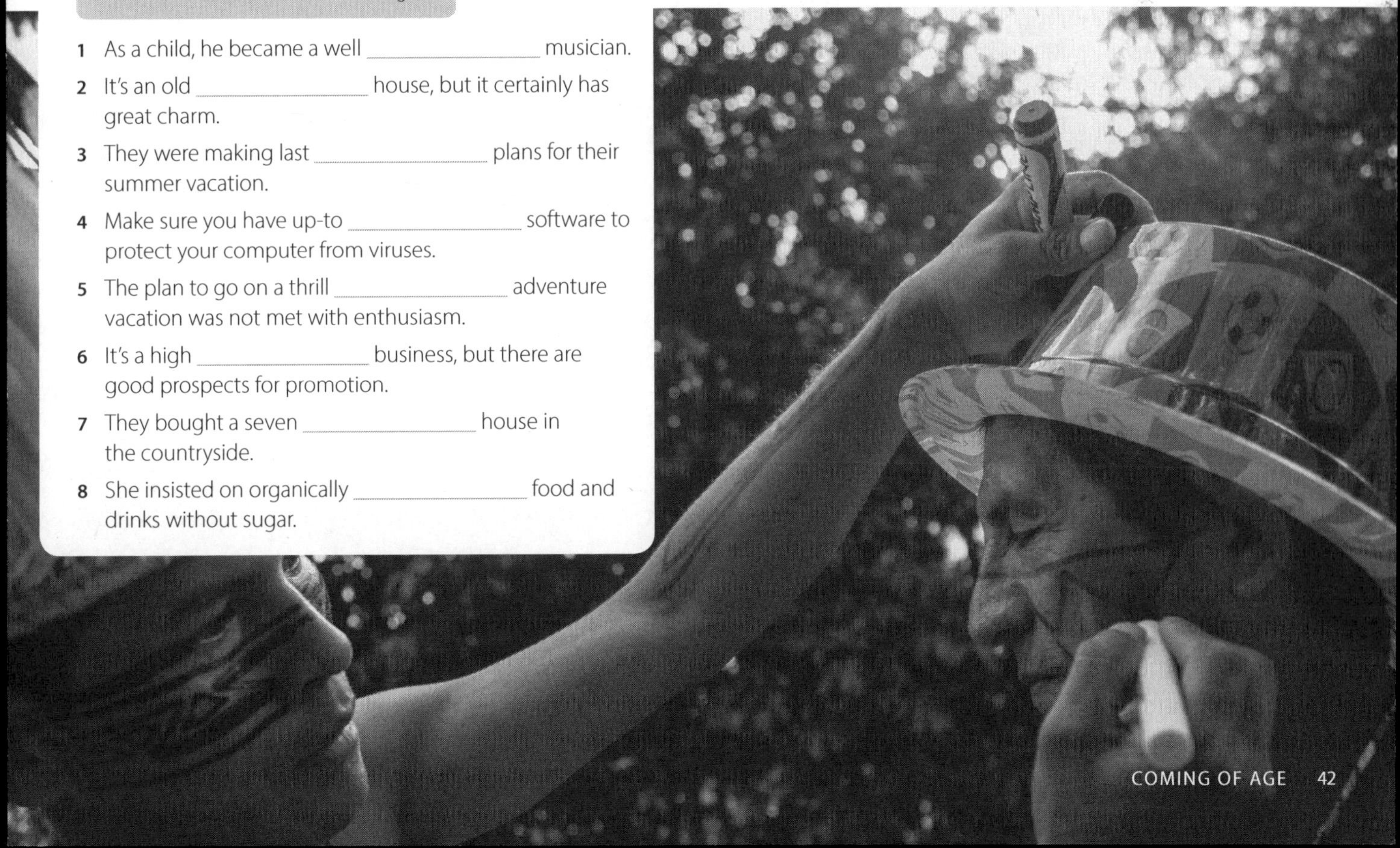

The happiest days of your LIFE?

I hadn't thought about [1] ________ much since I'd left, but on vacation last year, I found myself talking about my school days. I went to boarding school and, as it turned out, my experience was quite horrifying to the French girl that James and I were trying to impress.

What is a boarding school?

As the name says, 'boarding schools' are schools where students board, or live. Parents pay large amounts of money, believing that their precious boys will get the very best education and become awfully important. I say 'boys' because it was a single-sex boarding school; [2] ________ lived at the school during the semester and only went home during the holidays.

How to fit in

Part of going to a 'big' school is learning to fit in. We 'newbies' quickly had to learn school slang – 'chow' was food, 'uni' was uniform and so on. There were certain 'traditions', too, including physical 'tests' that you might consider barbaric. One of [3] ________ was to be thrown into a patch of sandspurs. Another was to make new boys swing from one end of the dorm roof to the other, which, given how high up [4] ________ were, was actually pretty dangerous. In fact, just before I left, this 'tradition' was banned after one boy broke his arm!

A long overdue change

Punishment is another aspect of my school life that seems to shock people. When I was a boy, teachers would paddle you on the behind if you did anything wrong. Our Head of School even kept a paddle on the bookshelf in his office that we called 'Big Bertha'. As of 2018, corporal punishment has been banned in public schools in 32 states, but only New Jersey and Iowa have banned [5] ________ in private schools. Big Bertha is gone from my old school—most parents these days object to paddling—but there is still no law to protect every student in every American school.

Routine

At my school, we had classes six days a week – waking up at six in the morning and working through until dinner. After dinner, there was study hall for two hours. There were no classes on Sundays and we were 'free' to leave school grounds as long as we were in uni. The uniforms we wore to class included striped neckties tied tight, thick blazers and itchy 'worsted wool' pants (to be honest, I still don't really know what [6] ________ is). On Sundays, though, uni was a polo shirt with the school crest and khaki pants.

Glossary

barbaric (adj) violent and cruel
corporal punishment (n) physical punishment of someone by hitting or beating them

READING

A PREDICT You are going to read about boys at an expensive boarding school in the US. What do you think the main differences are between their school experience and yours?

B SCAN Read *The happiest days of your life?* Were any of your ideas from Exercise A mentioned?

C PRONOUN REFERENCING Complete the article with an appropriate pronoun in each space. What does each pronoun refer to?

D READ FOR DETAIL Read the article again. Are these sentences true (T), false (F) or is the information not given (NG)?

1 The writer's friend James went to the same school as him. ***T/F/NG***
2 The writer thinks boarding schools offer the best education. ***T/F/NG***
3 The writer doesn't think the 'traditions' were violent. ***T/F/NG***
4 Corporal punishment has been banned from all public schools. ***T/F/NG***
5 Students could go elsewhere on Sundays. ***T/F/NG***
6 School uniforms were uncomfortable. ***T/F/NG***

E REFLECT Think about the answers to these questions.

1 Would you like to go to a boarding school like the one described in the text? Why/Why not?
2 Should education focus more on preparing students for their future careers or how to think for themselves? Why?

LISTENING

A You are going to listen to a conversation about homeschooling. List the main advantages and disadvantages of teaching children at home.

6.6 **B** **LISTEN FOR GIST** Listen to the conversation. Were any of your ideas from Exercise A mentioned?

6.6 **C** **LISTEN FOR DETAIL** Listen again and choose the correct options (a, b or c) to answer the questions.

1 When did the two women last see each other?
   a At least 12 years ago
   b Before Cleo moved to Philadelphia
   c At Cleo's wedding

2 How does Anya think home schooling will affect Cleo's children?
   a It will have a negative impact on their job prospects.
   b It will make it more difficult for them to get into college.
   c It will mean they aren't taught subjects like music and art.

3 Which subject is Cleo's husband best qualified to teach?
   a English literature
   b Science
   c Geography

4 How does Cleo ensure her curriculum is flexible?
   a She hires tutors to cover certain subjects.
   b She doesn't follow a mainstream grading system.
   c She allows her children to choose what to study.

5 Why did Cleo take her son out of high school?
   a Because he's shy and found it difficult to adapt
   b Because she felt he wasn't getting the skills he needed
   c Because he was treated badly by other children

6.7 **D** **DECODING IDIOMS** Listen to the extracts from the conversation. Are these sentences true (T) or false (F)? Correct the false sentences.

1 Anya says that her daughter's busy schedule is affecting her eating habits. ***T / F***

2 Anya thinks it will be difficult to cover such a wide range of subjects. ***T / F***

3 Cleo believes that homeschooling teaches students to think more creatively. ***T / F***

4 Cleo believes that most young people benefit from a college education. ***T / F***

5 Anya worries that the conversation has started badly. ***T / F***

E **REFLECT** Think about the answers to these questions.

1 Which of the two viewpoints put forward in the conversation do you agree with most? Why?

2 Why do you think some people choose to home school their children?

3 Do you agree with Cleo that homeschooled children can still get a good education? Why/Why not?

4 Do you think children should be allowed to decide what they study at school? Why/Why not?

5 When was the last time you felt like you had 'bitten off more than you could chew'? What happened in the end?

WRITING

A What do you think are some of the reasons for the rise and fall in popularity of certain subjects in college? Think about the following and write notes:

- changes in the educational system
- job prospects related to different subjects
- lack of interest
- lack of qualified teachers
- peer pressure

STUDENT NUMBERS

Introduction

[1]___ is to evaluate the results of a survey conducted to assess which college courses have shown the greatest increase or decline in enrolment, to suggest reasons for this trend and make certain recommendations.

Results

[2]___ the results of a survey conducted in colleges around the country. It clearly shows a marked decline in law and education courses, with 11,000 fewer enrollments in each. [3]___, languages have also suffered a significant decrease, given that numbers have been declining for many years.

[4]___, numbers for computer science have risen dramatically, as have those for business and management. This is partly a result of the new national curriculum which makes at least one science subject required, and partly due to the government's promotion of the sciences in education. [5]___ in enrollment was in computer science which is seen as being most suited to the modern workplace.

Interpretation

While the rise in those taking computer science, management and business is a positive development, the decline in the numbers of students taking languages and education is a cause for concern. Education is vital to a country's prospects and more educators are needed.

Recommendations

[6]___ that schools once again make at least one language required (as with science) and that more money be made available for education in the humanities. Schools encourage students to choose subjects suited to them rather than those that are currently popular or offer better job prospects. Some subjects are worth doing for themselves and form part of a complete education.

B Look at the bar chart showing the relative increase and decline in student numbers in certain subjects over a five-year period. Which subjects have seen the greatest decline? Which are the most popular subjects?

The biggest increases and drops in student numbers
Percentage change in number of students; top and bottom four over a five-year period

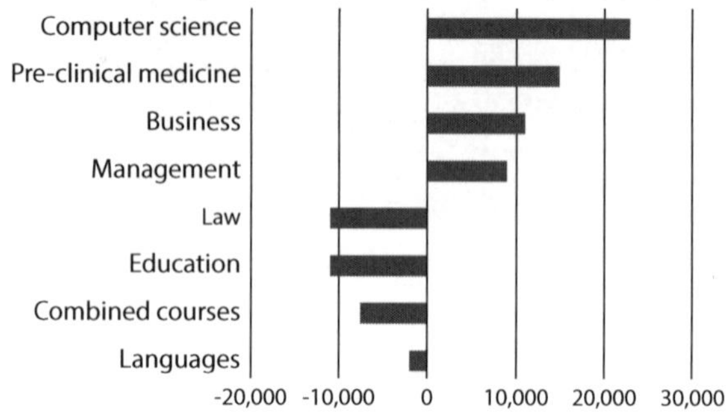

C **DESCRIBING DATA** Complete the report with the phrases (a–f).

a In contrast
b I would recommend
c The purpose of this report
d Similarly
e The graph illustrates
f The largest increase

WRITING PRACTICE

A **PLAN** You are going to write a report describing the data in the chart below and making recommendations about how to address the imbalance.

Subjects with the biggest gender divides

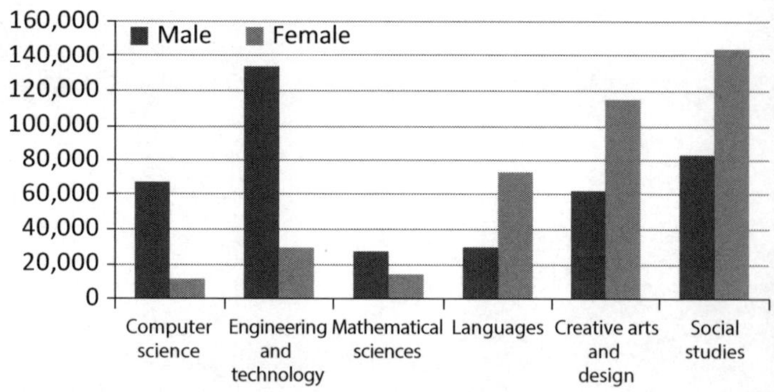

B **PREPARE** Organize your notes from Exercise A into a plan for a report.

C **WRITE** Write your report. Use your plan to help you.

D **EDIT** Edit your report. Check:

- spelling and punctuation
- report structure
- strength and analysis of ideas.

GRAMMAR

First conditional with different future forms; Unreal conditionals

A Choose the correct options (a, b or c) to complete the sentences.

1 What ___ if you win first prize?
   a do you do   b will you do   c did you do
2 If you ___, you won't meet the deadline.
   a don't hurry up   b won't hurry up   c 'll hurry up
3 They're going to start a community project if they ___ enough funding.
   a will get   b would get   c get
4 If everything goes according to plan, this time next year, I ___ in France.
   a 'll be living   b would live   c 'm living
5 As long as there are no more problems, I ___ by the end of the year.
   a finish   b have finished   c 'll have finished
6 OK, no problem. Just ___ me a call if you change your mind.
   a giving   b give   c gives
7 This ___ unless we all work together as a team.
   a shouldn't work   b won't work   c might work
8 If you need any further information, ___ our website.
   a will check   b check   c you will have checked

B Complete the sentences with the correct form of the verbs in parentheses. Use contractions where possible.

1 Sorry, I ________________ (*give*) you a lift if I'd known you were coming.
2 If I were you, I ________________ (*buy*) the tickets now – they always sell out really quickly.
3 Well, you ________________ (*be*) so tired if you'd gone to bed at a reasonable time last night.
4 If I ________________ (*have*) enough money, I'd build a house somewhere in the countryside.
5 I probably ________________ (*go*) to work for my dad if I hadn't gotten a job here.
6 My commute would be much easier if I ________________ (*have to*) change trains.

C Read the post and correct the mistakes in bold.

Douglas Bradshaw
3 hrs

As you know, the town council has achieved a great deal in the last year. In fact, I think it is fair to say that if we [1]**not taken** action, the community would have suffered greatly. It is certainly true that, if our members had not campaigned so effectively, we [2]**did not have** a bus service today and our town would be completely isolated.

Similarly, several of our oldest buildings could have been lost if we [3]**did not fought** to save them. Additionally, we [4]**might don't have** a community center today if generous members of the community had not stepped forward with the necessary funds. So, well done to everyone concerned!

However, there is more to be done. We [5]**could make** our town the pride of the region if we could. If we [6]**had had** the support of every member of our community, we could transform our town into a popular tourist destination and thriving residential area … and, needless to say, if we managed that, the value of each and every property [7]**went** up.

If we all contributed, there is no limit to what we could [8]**have achieved**. It is therefore in everyone's interest to come to our next meeting – date and venue to be announced soon. We look forward to seeing you all there.

Like | Comment | Share

VOCABULARY
Verbs to describe change

A Choose the correct options (a, b or c) to complete the sentences.

1 A new, 30-floor apartment building has been ___ near the subway station.
 a demolished **b** relocated **c** constructed
2 Our current site is too small, so we've decided ___ to the new business park outside town.
 a to convert **b** to relocate **c** to transform
3 The local council is ___ the disused factory into a homeless shelter.
 a restoring **b** constructing **c** converting
4 There used to be a multi-story parking garage on the site, but it was ___ two years ago.
 a demolished **b** restored **c** converted
5 The recreation center had fallen into disrepair, but it was ___ by a local team of volunteers.
 a constructed **b** relocated **c** restored
6 The redevelopment around the canal area of the city has completely ___ the area.
 a demolished **b** transformed **c** converted

B Complete the article with the correct form of the verbs in the box.

construct	demolish	extend
relocate	restore	transform

PRONUNCIATION
Connected speech in conditionals

7.1 **A Listen and circle the sentences you hear (a or b).**

1 **a** If I'd known about the problem in advance, I'd have planned for it.
 b If I know about the problem in advance, I plan for it.
2 **a** I think the customers would've paid more if we'd priced it lower.
 b I think the customers would pay more if we priced it lower.
3 **a** I'd help if he asked me.
 b I'd have helped if he'd asked me.
4 **a** If we'd had more customers, we'd have survived.
 b If we had more customers, we'd survive.
5 **a** We couldn't save the business even if we wanted to.
 b We couldn't have saved the business even if we'd wanted to.
6 **a** It might have been better if we'd invested less money.
 b It might be better if we invested less money.

7.2 **B Listen and repeat the sentences.**

1 I wouldn't have eaten the fish if I'd known it was undercooked.
2 If the concert had been cheaper, I probably would have gone.
3 If they had been friendlier, we might have hung out more.
4 The staff might have respected the boss more if she had listened to their feedback.

THE REVITALIZATION OF LARAMIE, WYOMING

Many major cities around the US have benefitted from revitalization projects – Detroit, Philadelphia, Pittsburgh, Nashville. However, some of the real success stories have happened on a much smaller scale. One of the best examples was the project [1] ____________ the sleepy railroad town of Laramie, Wyoming to its former glory.

Laramie was a 'tent town' on the eastern edge of the Rocky Mountains until Union Pacific's Laramie Train Depot was [2] ____________ in the 1860s. Work with the railroad, opportunities in the sheep and cattle businesses and the opening of the University of Wyoming enticed increasing numbers of settlers to this frontier town. In 1902, President Theodore Roosevelt established the Medicine Bow National Forest Preserve, which still attracts visitors to its million pristine acres.

By the end of the last century, though, historic downtown Laramie was in rough shape. Only two restaurants were still open, and many aging buildings were [3] ____________. With no incentive to venture further, college students stayed on campus and businesses went under.

That all changed in 2005, when the Wyoming Business Council provided funds and assistance to create a Laramie Main Street Alliance. Their first step was to move a planned art exhibit from one building on campus to several public spaces downtown. The exhibit lured students off campus, exposed local residents to art and inspired Laramie's award-winning Mural Project.

For the project, local artists [4] ____________ the walls of drab buildings with large-scale images reflecting the area's natural beauty and cultural heritage. As a result, visitor numbers increased, small businesses in the suburbs decided [5] ____________ to downtown and new restaurants opened to serve their employees. The Mural Project's success [6] ____________ to every aspect of the community's revitalization. The historic area now spans 30 blocks and boasts not only restaurants and retailers, but also apartments and a nonprofit grocery store that sells products from local ranches and farms.

GRAMMAR
Wish and *if only*

A Find and correct six mistakes with *wish* and *if only* in Alexis's comment.

Culture Shock
8 mins

The end of the year is a time for reflection. A time to think about your biggest wishes and regrets. So let us help you get things off your chest. Leave a comment below for your chance to win a year's subscription to Culture Shock.

Like | Comment | Share

Alexis
20 mins

I wish I've done things a little differently when I was younger. If only I tried a little bit harder as a student, I would have gotten a much better degree. And that would have led to a better job. If only I do a job that I could be proud of, but I don't – it's just boring! To be honest, I wish people won't ask me what I do for a living because I'm ashamed that it's just … well … nothing very impressive. I also sometimes wish I've been braver with my life decisions in the past. I mean, I've lived and worked in the same town all my life. If only I would have the courage to try something and somewhere else when I was younger.

Like | Comment | Share

B Choose the correct options (a, b or c) to complete the sentences.

1 I wish I ___ someone who could help me get a job in the publishing industry.
   a know **b** knew **c** known
2 If only I ___ that I wanted an adventure – none of this would have happened.
   a hadn't decided **b** haven't decided **c** didn't decide
3 I wish those people next door ___ shouting at each other!
   a stop **b** stopped **c** would stop
4 If only I ___ a little more money, I could rent somewhere nicer to live.
   a had **b** have **c** have had
5 I wish I ___ travel with my job – just once a month would be nice.
   a would **b** could **c** should
6 If only we ___ all our money on that pizza, we would be able to get a taxi home.
   a didn't spend **b** hadn't spent **c** wouldn't spend
7 I wish the weather ___ nicer here – then it would be the perfect place to live.
   a is **b** would be **c** were
8 If only we ___ some warning that this was coming – we wouldn't have lost the business.
   a had had **b** were having **c** have had

VOCABULARY
Three-part phrasal verbs; Compound nouns

A Replace the words in bold with the three-part phrasal verbs in the box.

come up against   come up with
cut down on   get around to   get along with
keep up with   look up to   run out of

1 When are you going to **find the time to start** going to the gym?
2 We seem to have **used up all the** shampoo. Can you buy some more?
3 We're half-way through the project; we've **hit** a problem.
4 Is there anyone in politics that you **admire**?
5 We need to **think of** a better name for the product.
6 If you don't **stay informed about** the latest developments in this industry, you quickly lose out to the competition.
7 I don't **have a good relationship with** Lizzie. I'd rather not have her on my team.
8 I think it's important for all of us to **reduce** the amount of sugar we eat.

B Choose the correct options to complete the sentences.

1 Car *parking* / *sharing* systems mean that the roads aren't blocked with cars carrying only one occupant.
2 Noise *pollution* / *level* is a dangerous or annoying amount of noise, often caused by traffic.
3 Community *spirit* / *life* is the feeling of togetherness and willingness for a community to work together.
4 It's common for communities in the US to organize a street *party* / *procession* for events such as the Fourth of July.
5 Food *banks* / *retailers* are non-profit organizations that distribute food to those in need.
6 A youth *theater* / *group* organizes social events and activities for young people in a community.
7 Facilities such as community gardens often rely on volunteer *workers* / *caregivers*.
8 A language *exchange* / *course* is when two speakers meet to teach each other their languages.

PRONUNCIATION
Two-stress phrasal verbs

7.3 **A** Listen to the sentences. Where is the main stress on the phrasal verbs? Where is the secondary stress?

1 We **came up against** quite a few problems early on.
2 You need to **stand up for** your beliefs.
3 I can't **keep up with** all these changes.
4 They **teamed up with** people from another company.
5 During the holidays, I like to **catch up with** my friends.
6 I **get along with** most of the people in my department.

7.4 **B** Listen to each sentence said in two different ways. Choose the sentence (a or b) in which the phrasal verb is stressed correctly.

1 I think you need to **stand up for** yourself a bit more. *a* / *b*
2 Who's going to **take care of** you if you're sick? *a* / *b*
3 We could always **team up with** one of the big fast food chains. *a* / *b*
4 I need to **take care of** my grandma; she's not doing so well at the moment. *a* / *b*
5 He doesn't really **get along with** his sister. *a* / *b*
6 We don't go jogging anymore – I just can't **keep up with** her! *a* / *b*
7 I **caught up with** an old friend from school last night. *a* / *b*

READING

A Read the definition and list the main advantages and disadvantages of this type of community.

> **co-housing (n)** a community of private homes built around shared spaces (e.g. dining areas, laundry rooms, etc), in which residents usually share work (e.g. growing crops, taking care of children, etc)

B READ FOR GIST Skim *Alternative communities* and choose the best summary (1, 2 or 3) of the writer's opinion on co-housing projects.

1 They work for some people but are unsuitable for families.

2 They offer a range of benefits, especially to those who feel isolated.

3 They are a passing trend that cannot survive in the modern world.

C IDENTIFY SPECULATION Read the article again and answer the questions.

1 Why does the writer think co-housing is so popular in the US?

2 Does the writer think more OWCH projects will be set up soon?

3 Why does the writer believe some co-living projects failed?

4 Why does the writer think combining living and work spaces might prove unpopular?

D INFER MEANING Read the article again. Match the underlined sentences (1–4) to the implied meanings (a–f). There are two more options than you need.

a They would probably take offense.

b I couldn't think of anything worse.

c I wouldn't want to do it again.

d I had been rude.

e I could think of worse things to say.

f The people he talked to didn't like the implications.

E REFLECT Think about the answers to these questions.

1 Would you like to live in any of the projects described in the article?

2 What do you think makes a successful community?

Alternative communities

Perhaps I should change the title of my article to 'Communities of choice', because every time I use the word 'alternative', [1]<u>I am gently but firmly corrected</u>. I think the reason why some people don't like the word is that it suggests dropping out of society rather than finding a way to fit in – avoiding the 'normal' way of life as if there's something wrong with it. I'm not sure I agree with this, but I would say that the term isn't quite accurate enough. Some of the communities I looked into were – [2]<u>and I'm being polite</u> – impractical: living in treehouses, caves, underground and so on. So I'll focus on a specific type of alternative community – co-housing. It's a big trend around the world, especially in the US. (It seems as if Americans are always looking for life hacks, or new ways to manage their daily activities.). The movement, in one form or another, seems to offer a genuine answer to the problems of social isolation, community decline and urban planning which so many people complain of in modern society.

[3]<u>Three years in shared housing as a student has somewhat colored my view of communal living</u>, but I can see the attraction of co-housing for some. Co-housing systems are open to everyone, though groups of people with a common interest can start their own. Basically, the idea is that a group of people get together along with architects and urban planners to come up with a design for the community they want. This can mean starting right from the beginning with a new housing development or renovating or restoring existing buildings. Usually there is a common house at the center of the community where people can meet, cook, eat together, do their laundry and so on and a shared space outside for gardens and children to play in. Essentially, the whole area is designed to encourage social interaction.

One of the less conventional examples is the Older Women's Cohousing Community (OWCH). [4]You could call it an old people's home, but I wouldn't if I were you, not when you're talking to one of its residents. These women look out for each other, and years of struggle to get the system off the ground has made them resilient. Here there are shared spaces – a garden, recreational facilities and so on – and they take turns working outside, cooking and cleaning. However, unlike more traditional communes, the women either rent or buy their apartments. Their hope is that many other groups like theirs will emerge, but how likely is this? It takes time, money (a lot of it), the cooperation of various local authorities and the kind of toughness not everyone has. But their energy and enthusiasm are infectious, so who knows?

Then there are the systems designed for millennials. Apparently, in New York the co-living business is booming – though several companies have tried to set up co-living systems and failed. My guess is that it was too much like living in a hotel for many people. Small apartments fully furnished – down to even the toiletries – around communal spaces are made available at competitive prices. Now some companies are combining the living space and the workplace into one. This may appeal to the sociable, get-ahead, young professional – they can make contacts, discuss business ideas and have a good time all in one space – but, again, I can't help but wonder how successful this will prove. Surely most people want to keep their private lives, well, separate from work?

Whichever form co-housing takes, one thing remains constant – for many of the tenants, communities like these help to relieve the feelings of social isolation they felt in the modern urban environment. While I personally wouldn't choose to call any of these communities home, I can appreciate the value they add to our society as a whole.

LISTENING

7.5 **A LISTEN FOR GIST** Listen to the introduction to a talk about urban development and answer the questions.

1 What was the topic of the previous talk?

2 Why are architects developing underground projects?

7.6 **B LISTEN FOR ORGANIZATION** Listen to the next part of the talk. Put the topics in the order they are discussed.

___ Solving a transportation issue

___ Repurposing an industrial facility

___ Housing an underground farm

___ Keeping things safe and secure

___ Creating an artificial climate

7.6 **C LISTEN FOR DETAIL** Listen to the second part of the talk again. Complete the notes below with no more than three words or a number.

Growing Underground

City: 1 ________

Location: Old underground 2 ________

Main activity: Growing 3 ________ and ________

Main advantages:

- Low 4 ________ and ________ consumption
- Constant temperature
- Low transportation-related pollution

Subtropolis

City: Kansas City

Location: an inactive 5 ________

Main uses: offices and 6 ________ premises

Main advantages:

- Constant temperature
- saves money on 7 ________
- secure location

Bicycle park

City: 8 ________

Location: Under one of the central 9 ________

Main activity: Bike storage/parking

Main advantages:

- Saves space on the streets
- Protects bicycle owners from vandalism and 10 ________

D REFLECT Think about the answers to these questions.

1 What other uses for underground facilities can you think of?

2 How else could cities address the issue of overcrowding?

7.5 Community
Write a formal letter of complaint

WRITING

A Skim the letter and answer the questions.

1 Why has the writer written the letter?
2 Who is the letter for?
3 What features make the letter formal?

B Read the letter again. Match the paragraphs (1–3) to their functions (a–c).

Paragraph 1	**a** a request for action
Paragraph 2	**b** reasons for writing
Paragraph 3	**c** what the issues are

Dear Sir/Madam,

I am writing to you with regard to the Council's proposal to close the local library and to build more retirement homes on the site. While I applaud the Council's efforts to provide housing and care for the elderly, [1]*I don't agree* that it should mean the loss of such an important social institution.

[2]*I know* that local councils are under a lot of pressure to make cuts, and I am aware that fewer people these days use the library than they used to, but it would be a great shame to lose it completely. I have no doubt that if it offered more activities and educational programs for young children, more people would use it. [3]*I think* the proposal would do more harm than good. [4]*Can't you find* an alternative site for the retirement homes? The old office block on Church Street is due for demolition; perhaps this would be suitable for renovation into apartments. Local residents feel strongly on this matter and are organizing to oppose your proposal.

[5]*It is* in everyone's interests if you consulted local residents about this matter and gave their opinion a fair consideration. I look forward to hearing from you on this matter.

Sincerely,

Marjorie Smith

C HEDGING Read again. Replace the phrases in italics (1–5) with the more formal hedging phrases (a–e).

a May I suggest
b I'm afraid I can't agree
c I'm sorry, but I think
d I feel it would be
e I appreciate

WRITING PRACTICE

A PREPARE Write a list of issues in your town or city (e.g. graffiti, lack of housing, poor transportation links, etc).

B PLAN Choose one of the issues from Exercise A to write a letter of complaint about. Write notes and organize them into a plan for a formal letter.

C WRITE Write your letter of complaint in 150–250 words. Use your plan to help you.

D EDIT Edit your letter. Check:

- spelling and punctuation
- strength of analysis and recommendations
- use of hedging language.

GRAMMAR

Past modals of deduction

A Complete the article with past modals of deduction and the correct form of the verbs in parentheses.

The disappearance of Amelia Earhart

On July 2, 1937, Amelia Earhart left Papua New Guinea in her aircraft and headed for Howland Island. However, she never arrived, and no trace of her, her plane or her navigator, Fred Noonan, have ever been found. The easiest conclusion to draw is that they [1] ______________ (*crash*) into the sea. In their search for the island, they [2] ______________ (*get*) lost and, according to most theories, [3] ______________ (*run out*) of fuel before they could land. Suggestions that the unfortunate pair [4] ______________ (*capture*) by Japanese soldiers are based on pure guesswork and have no supporting evidence. Some bones were found on a different island, suggesting that they [5] ______________ (*reach*) land, only to be killed by wild animals or die from their injuries. Other findings in the area have led to suggestions that their remains [6] ______________ (*find*), but each time, the evidence has been inconclusive. More recent examination of the remains can only conclude that they [7] ______________ (*be*) those of a man or a woman, but we can't be entirely certain. The mystery remains unsolved, and the only thing we can say with any certainty is that it [8] ______________ (*be*) a pleasant end for the two aviators.

B Rewrite the sentences in bold using appropriate past modals of deduction.

1 She hasn't arrived yet. **Maybe she has gotten lost.**
She ______________.

2 **I'm certain that Don didn't steal the money.** He wasn't there at the time.
Don ______________.

3 **I'm sure that the package arrived** because I tracked it online.
The ______________.

4 **There's a chance that the plane was delayed.** It hasn't arrived yet.
The ______________.

5 **It's impossible that Tom was born in 1976.** He only looks about 30.
Tom ______________.

6 **I'm sure the car was stolen.** It's gone and there is smashed glass in the parking space.
My ______________.

7 **It wasn't Stephen that you saw** because he's in Austria.
It ______________.

8 **Perhaps they were French.** One of them mentioned their apartment in Paris.
They ______________.

VOCABULARY
Word families

A Complete the word families in the table.

verb	noun	adjective	adverb
–	tradition	1	2
3	4	believable	believably
–	–	essential	5
mythologize	6	7	–
–	8	legendary	9
10	resemblance	–	–
11	representation	12	–

B Complete the article with the correct form of the words in Exercise A.

Beware of the WATER

Inuit children grow up living very close to ice and water. While the ocean is a great source of food for these people, the freezing cold Artic waters are also very dangerous for young children in the community. That's why parents share a warning story with their children about a [1] ______________ creature called a Qalupalik that can be found near the water's edge.

[2] ______________ has it that the Qalupalik is a half-human creature that [3] ______________ an evil mermaid. They are [4] ______________ described as having long hair, long fingernails, a female face and green skin. They live close to the coastline and lie in wait to catch naughty children who roam too close to the water. When they catch a child, they put them in a pouch and carry them deep under water, never to return.

Qalupaliks are [5] ______________ in different ways depending on the story. Some say that they keep children in a secret place, others say that they eat them and some even suggest that as the captive children age, the Qalupalik gets younger. Either way, none of the stories are that pleasant, and children who [6] ______________ this [7] ______________ would be very likely to avoid walking too close to the shore!

Qalupaliks are [8] ______________ an Inuit version of the bogeyman. They often appear in popular culture in Canada and other Arctic regions. If you're walking along the coast near the Arctic Circle, then be warned – you can always identify a Qalupalik by its distinctive sound, which is like an eerie hum …

PRONUNCIATION
Thought groups

8.1 **A** **Listen to the text about an Irish folk hero and mark the pauses with a (/).**

In Irish folklore, Cúchulainn is a mythological hero who appears in many stories. According to the stories, during battles, he is transformed into some kind of monster. Although descriptions of him differ in the various stories, most agree that he is extremely handsome. The stories about Cúchulainn bear some similarity to other legends from different parts of the world, most notably ancient Greece and Persia.

8.2 **B** **Read the last part of the story. Mark where you think the speaker will pause with a (/). Then listen and check.**

Cúchulainn's most heroic deed was performed at the Raid of Cooley. Legend has it, the Irish hero defended Ulster from attack from the men of Connaught. The leader of Connaught, Queen Medb, wanted to conquer Ulster so she could take possession of a magical brown bull, which was owned by the elder warriors of Ulster.

At the time of the attack, the men of Ulster were suffering from a bizarre weakness imposed on them by the goddess Macha. None of the warriors were able to defend their city. Cúchulainn, however, was unaffected by Macha's curse as he was not merely human – he was the son of a god.

Cúchulainn went to battle against the whole army of Connaught, helped only by his father, the god of light, and by Morrigan, the goddess of war. During the defense, Cúchulainn is severely wounded, but his father helps heal his wounds. He regains his energy and kills hundreds of Connaught soldiers, using their dead bodies to build a wall to help defend Ulster. Eventually, the men of Ulster regain strength and launch into battle, forcing their enemy to retreat.

VOCABULARY
Easily confused verbs; Crime

A Choose the correct options to complete the story.

As Gerard got out of bed, he stopped and [1]***listened / heard*** for a moment. Something didn't seem quite right and he wanted to be sure. From the woods surrounding the house, he [2]***listened / heard*** a dog barking, but nothing else. 'I must be [3]***listening / hearing*** things,' he thought to himself. He got dressed and stood [4]***watching / looking*** out of the window at the trees. It [5]***felt / touched*** cold – cold enough for snow – but so far there was no sign of it. As he was [6]***seeing / watching*** the treetops swaying in the breeze, he [7]***saw / watched*** something else. It was smoke. Very quickly, the awful realization dawned on him that the house was on fire. Rushing to the door of his bedroom, he felt the back of it to see if it was hot. It wasn't, so he gently opened it and [8]***saw / looked*** out into the hallway. There were no flames, but the air was thick with smoke and he couldn't see. He made his way toward the staircase, then quickly ran down the stairs. He grabbed the door handle to fling the door open and escape, but as his hand [9]***touched / felt*** it, he screamed in pain! It was metal and had been heated by the fire. Gerard turned around and [10]***watched / looked*** for another way to escape, but the smoke was blurring everything. He felt so disorientated in his own home, and he was beginning to feel dizzy …

B Match the crime vocabulary (1–6) to the scenarios (a–f).

1 burglary ___
2 bribe ___
3 identity theft ___
4 robbery ___
5 fraud ___
6 blackmail ___

a Ms. Smith returned home to find her front door had been kicked open and all of her valuables missing.

b Someone has used my bank details to order a new phone, laptop and wireless headphones online! Unbelievable!

c They said that if I didn't give them $1,000, they would sell the photographs to a newspaper.

d He had been claiming disability benefits for years because he could not walk. When investigators visited his house, they saw him playing soccer in the yard!

e They ran into the store and told everybody to get down. Then they ran behind the counter, demanded that the register was opened and started taking the money.

f They said that if we give them the contract, they will offer us free tickets to big soccer games. They keep sending us presents to persuade us to sign the deal.

C Complete the sentences with the correct form of the words in the box.

accuse catch charge commit innocent investigate proof punishment question sentence witness

1 I don't think prison is a suitable __________ for minor crimes such as vandalism.

2 The judge __________ him to nine months in prison.

3 There were two key __________ to the robbery on Oak Street.

4 Police are __________ a possible break-in at Mear's Garage on Warren Street.

5 He was __________ of theft after three members of the staff reported having possessions stolen from their lockers.

6 The suspect fled the scene but was later __________, arrested and __________ with dangerous driving.

7 She was sent to prison for a crime she didn't __________. It was a high-profile miscarriage of justice.

8 The trial lasted two months, but eventually the defendant was proven __________.

9 There wasn't enough __________ to convict the suspect of murder.

10 The suspects were taken to the police station where they were __________ for three hours, then released.

GRAMMAR
Order of adjectives

A Rewrite the sentences using the adjectives in parentheses.

1 We watched a documentary on Netflix last night. (*Japanese/interesting*)

______

2 She was wearing a shirt she bought on sale. (*cotton/striped*)

______

3 They live in a house just outside Charleston. (*fantastic/old*)

______

4 The clock struck midnight as he tiptoed down the stairs. (*antique/wooden*)

______

5 Overall, I'd say that it's quite a car. (*little/economical*)

______

6 Apparently, she's found a dress she likes. (*beautiful/Italian*)

______

7 As I stood up, an object on the grass caught my eye. (*small/round*)

______

8 Every day, he ate two doughnuts for breakfast. (*sugar-coated/large*)

______

9 The $20 million development includes two lecture theaters. (*state-of-the-art/large*)

______

10 The couple found the vase in their backyard. (*Chinese/16th century*)

______

B Are these correct or incorrect? Rewrite the incorrect sentences.

1 It's a coastal charming little town on Cape Cod.
2 It was a rare, 19th-century landscape painting.
3 I bought a designer new suit for my interview.
4 At the entrance was a large, imposing wooden door.
5 She's tall with blond shoulder-length hair.
6 We live on a long tree-lined pleasant street in the suburbs.
7 The castle was full of priceless, medieval artifacts.
8 We were struck by the snow-covered beautiful hills.

PRONUNCIATION
Adding information

8.3 **A Listen to the sentences. Does the speaker use a falling (↘), rising (↗) or fall-rising (↘↗) tone on the underlined parts of the sentences?**

1 There was no evidence of a forced entry into the house. <u>On top of that</u>, there seemed to be nothing missing.
2 There was nothing linking the man to the murder, but he didn't protest his innocence. <u>In fact</u>, he seemed eager to sign a full confession.
3 Critics argue that criminals rarely serve their full sentences. <u>Furthermore</u>, they point to statistics showing that many go on to reoffend.

8.4 **B Listen and repeat the sentences.**

1 You would think prison would change his behavior. <u>But actually</u>, he committed far worse crimes after release.
2 It's clear that our memories can be altered. <u>On top of that</u>, entirely new memories can be created.
3 CCTV shows Mr. Duncan was in the area at the time of the robbery. <u>Furthermore</u>, he had a clear motive for involvement.

READING

A PREDICT Look at the clipping from an old newspaper and the picture. Can you think of an explanation for what might have happened?

MYSTERY OF THE MARY CELESTE

Ship found abandoned at sea, but entire crew vanished without a trace.

B READ FOR MAIN IDEAS Read *Mary Celeste: the ghost ship* and check your ideas from Exercise A.

C READ FOR MAIN IDEAS Read the article again. Are these statements true (T), false (F) or not given (NG)? Correct the false sentences.

1. Conan Doyle chose to present his own version of events. *T / F / NG*
2. The abandoned ship was found just under a month after it had left New York. *T / F / NG*
3. The ship had completely run out of provisions. *T / F / NG*
4. The writer thinks that a pirate attack is the most likely explanation. *T / F / NG*
5. The writer argues that not knowing what happened makes the story more interesting. *T / F / NG*
6. The chronometer and pump both stopped working in bad weather. *T / F / NG*

D DECODE: SIMILES AND METAPHORS Read the article again and answer the questions.

1. What does the writer compare the *Mary Celeste* with when it was discovered?
2. Why do you think the writer used that image?
3. What does the line *'papers lay about like confetti'* suggest?

E REFLECT Think about the answers to these questions.

1. What do you think is the most likely explanation to the mystery of the *Mary Celeste*?
2. Do you believe that there is a rational explanation for every mystery?

MARY CELESTE:

the ghost ship

The story of the *Mary Celeste* might not have become so well-known if Arthur Conan Doyle, the English writer famous for creating the fictional detective Sherlock Holmes, hadn't written a short story based on the mysterious events of 1872. His story was so convincing that many people believed it to be a true account of events. In Conan Doyle's version, the ship is discovered floating in the Atlantic Ocean in perfect condition, with a half-finished meal on the table and the coffee still warm in the mugs. It was as if the crew had just left.

That, however, was fiction. But what is known about the event is no less strange, and what might have happened remains a cause of endless speculation. What we do know is that the ship set sail from New York on November 7, 1872, with ten people on board: Captain Benjamin Briggs, his wife and daughter and a seven-member crew. The ship was discovered on December 5th, like a bottle which had been thrown into the sea, hundreds of miles off the coast of Portugal. But this bottle had no message in it. It wasn't in the condition described by Doyle in his fictionalized account, but neither was it badly damaged. Papers lay about like confetti and the ship had taken on some water, and one of the ship's pumps was found in pieces as if being repaired – but there was no abandoned dinner. The crew's belongings were still there, there were supplies of food and water and the cargo was in place. But the captain, his family and the crew were nowhere to be found. The ship's only lifeboat was missing. The last entry in the ship's log was made at 5 am on November 25th.

So what are the theories? First, let's look at the least likely. There are some who think it must have been an alien abduction, perhaps inspired by Doyle's suggestion of interrupted activity. Slightly less silly, but only slightly, are those who speculate that it could have been a sea monster of some kind, such as a giant squid: but they tend to stay deep underwater, and anyway wouldn't it have taken the whole ship down with it? Others suggest that the ship might have been attacked by pirates, not as improbable as the other theories, but it's unlikely to have been the reason – they would have taken the cargo. Freak weather conditions is another possibility, but in that case, wouldn't there have been more damage to the ship?

We will probably never know what happened, which is why it remains so fascinating. Mysteries like this allow our imaginations to run wild, but the truth is often far less interesting. So far, the most plausible explanation is that the ship might have gone off course because of rough seas and a faulty chronometer. The ship had also been taking on water – remember the pump found in pieces? – so it's possible that the captain, unable to fully assess the amount of water pouring into the ship, and with a pump not working, might have given the order to abandon ship fearing that it would sink. They got into the lifeboat and, still attached to the ship by a rope, waited to see if the ship would sink. Maybe the rope broke or came loose, leaving them at the mercy of the waves.

Glossary

abduction (n) being taken away by force, kidnapped
chronometer (n) piece of equipment that measures time accurately

LISTENING

A PREDICT Which of these genres of fiction do you think is the most popular in the US? Why?

- science fiction and fantasy
- romance
- crime/mystery
- literary fiction

8.5 **B LISTEN FOR GIST** Listen to an interview with a successful author and check your answers from Exercise A.

8.5 **C LISTEN FOR ORGANIZATION** Listen again. Put the topics in the order they are discussed.

___ Excitement keeps you entertained
___ Bringing order to chaos
___ The basic structure of a crime novel
___ Sales are at their highest ever
___ Creating an ideal moral world

8.5 **D FOLLOW AN ARGUMENT** Listen again and choose the correct options (a, b or c) to complete the sentences.

1 The speaker argues that most crime novels are similar because they …
  a center around an unsolved murder.
  b involve a main character with artistic tendencies.
  c have a plot which follows a standard formula.

2 According to the speaker, the most important factor for readers is …
  a an exciting storyline.
  b expressive writing.
  c an attractive cover.

3 According to the speaker, many people find that crime fiction …
  a explains the psychology of evil people.
  b offers a moral message.
  c reflects their view of justice.

4 The Oscar Wilde quote supports the speaker's argument because …
  a it shows that Oscar Wilde wrote about themes of good and evil.
  b it suggests that fiction does not reflect harsh reality.
  c it offers advice on how to create good writing.

5 The speaker believes that crime fiction …
  a helps us to resolve our own problems.
  b offers us reassurance and order.
  c accurately reflects real life.

E REFLECT Think about the answers to these questions.

1 Which of the genres of fiction listed in Exercise A do you enjoy most? Why?

2 Can you think of reasons why people enjoy those genres? Are those reasons similar or different to the ones which the speaker mentioned in her talk?

8.5 Mystery

Write a complex essay

WRITING

A Read the essay prompt and answer the questions.

> Cybercrime – offenses such as identity theft and credit card fraud – now tops the list of criminal activity around the world. What might account for the rise in cybercrime? And what measures can we take to protect ourselves against it?

1. What themes do you have to address?
2. Does 'it' in the last sentence of the prompt refer to identity theft, cybercrime or credit card fraud?

B Read the introduction and body of the essay. Choose the correct options (a, b or c) to answer the questions.

1. What is the main cause of the rise in cybercrime?
   - a The internet is a global phenomenon.
   - b People don't know about security measures.
   - c People put data which is attractive to criminals online.
2. What is the most effective way to reduce cybercrime?
   - a To inform the police when you've been hacked.
   - b Individuals should provide security for their own data.
   - c Educating the young.

> Cybercrime has become the most widespread criminal activity in the world. This essay will first focus on why crimes such as identity theft and computer fraud are on the rise and then suggest ways of protecting ourselves against them.
>
> There are a number of reasons for the rise in this type of crime. The foremost problem is that we put so much personal information online that it is easy for criminals to acquire banking or credit card details and hack into people's bank accounts. Second, there is the problem that many people are unaware of how to protect that information. A further major problem – which the individual can do little about – is that computer networks now cover the globe, and as a result, it is very difficult for the authorities to actually police cybercrime.
>
> The best way to tackle the problem is to be responsible for ourselves. We should make sure that our online information is well-protected, using firewalls and antivirus software. Another solution is education – teaching children of the dangers as soon as they start using computers. The police can help to a limited extent – they can provide information on how best to protect yourself – and you should inform them immediately if you have been the victim of identity theft or your bank account has been hacked and let them deal with the problem.

C WRITING CONCLUSIONS Which is the best conclusion for the essay in Exercise B?

> **1**
> In conclusion, we have only ourselves to blame for the rise in cybercrime, by putting so much personal information online where it is easily acquired by cybercriminals and used to hack into bank accounts. We rely on the authorities to deal with the problem when we should be taking personal responsibility. People need to be educated as early as possible on how to protect their online data: this would go some way in reducing the number of crimes committed.

> **2**
> In conclusion, the very success of the internet, its global reach and the fact that we put so much personal information into the public sphere all contribute to the rise in cybercrime. It also makes it difficult to catch those responsible for criminal activity. The best solution for now is to educate people from an early age on how to protect their online presence by using, for example, firewalls and antivirus software. This means taking personal responsibility for our cybersecurity.

WRITING PRACTICE

A PREPARE Read the essay prompt below and write notes about how to answer it.

> Cyber bullying is rapidly growing into a major problem for young people today. What are some of the reasons for its growth? And what can be done to prevent it?

B PLAN Organize your notes into a plan for an essay.

C WRITE Write your essay. Use your plan to help you.

D EDIT Edit your essay. Check:

- spelling and punctuation
- use of language
- strength of ideas.

9.1 Business

Customers

GRAMMAR
Adjective clauses

A Choose the correct options to complete the sentences.

1 The company, ***which*** / ***that*** was founded in 1971, serves an estimated four million cups of coffee a day.

2 Almost all the consumers – / ***that*** previewed the product were dissatisfied.

3 Overall, he was fairly satisfied with the company ***where*** / ***that*** he worked for.

4 Saturation is a situation ***for when*** / ***in which*** the availability of a product or service in a market has been maximized.

5 The place ***where*** / ***that*** the store was located meant it didn't get much foot traffic.

6 The mystery shopper, ***which*** / ***who*** will visit the store sometime this week, should provide us with some useful feedback.

7 Do you remember the customer – / ***that*** complained about the lack of parking near the store last week? Well, he's back. Can you deal with him?

8 I remember the days ***when*** / ***where*** we didn't have these fancy shopping malls – it was all main streets and local businesses.

9 The well-known grocery store, ***who*** / ***whose*** profits slumped during the first quarter, has announced that they are calling in the administrators.

10 The way ***which*** / – the toy company handled the product recall received negative attention from the press.

11 The company's new electric car, ***that*** / ***which*** costs $27,000, takes over 21 hours to fully charge.

12 There's the restaurant – / ***where*** I'm taking Nicky to on Saturday night.

B Combine the sentences using an adjective clause. Omit the relative pronoun where possible.

1 We watched a documentary last night. It was terrible!

____

2 Could you pass me the book? The one on the table.

____

3 The first stop on our journey was Ljubljana. It is the capital of Slovenia.

____

4 My friend just started dating a guy. I used to work with him.

____

5 Hey, that's the man! He stole my purse!

____

C Are these sentences correct or incorrect? Rewrite the incorrect sentences.

1 The employee dealt with me in the store was really helpful.

2 Online sales that have increased dramatically over the last year, could be our main source of income soon.

3 We haven't been back to the restaurant when we ate that bad shrimp.

4 I don't know whose to blame for the poor promotional campaign.

5 The ideal candidate for the role would be someone who has excellent customer service skills.

6 In my opinion, retailers that refuse to ban plastic bags should be fined.

7 I've no time for managers who sole focus is maximizing profit.

8 Not one of the employees in which he hired had the right attributes – I'd seriously question his recruitment process.

9.1 Business

Customers

PRONUNCIATION
Pitch on non-essential adjective clauses

9.1 **A Listen to the sentences. Does the speaker's pitch step up or down on the non-essential adjective clause?**

1. The weather app, which I use more than any other, is really very good.
2. The free version of Spotify, which does contain advertising, is still worth having.
3. Radio, which everyone expected to die out, is actually as popular as ever.
4. Athens, where I grew up, has some really great places to visit.
5. This product, which was only launched last week, is selling by the millions!
6. Marge, who is a doctor, lives on the same block as me.

9.2 **B Listen and repeat the sentences.**

1. The staff member, who was on a temporary contract at the time, was dismissed immediately.
2. The company, which was established in the early 20th century, continues to be a world leader in the entertainment industry.
3. Magnolia Bakery, which is based near Savannah, is a local supplier of pastry and other baked goods.
4. The pension plan, which has declined in popularity over the years, is to be phased out by 2022.
5. Investors from Japan, where cryptocurrency is commonplace, believe this could be the future of global trade.

VOCABULARY
Dependent prepositions: verbs

A Choose the correct options to complete the sentences.

1. Company representatives must adhere *to / for* a strict dress code when meeting clients.
2. I can't do the weekly shopping with my partner – we always argue *for / about* what to buy.
3. I don't think dealing *on / with* complaints over the phone is one of her strengths.
4. Thank you *for / with* your interest in our company and we wish you the best of luck with your job search.
5. I'd like to complain *at / about* the service at your restaurant tonight. It has been below the usual standard.
6. I'm sorry, but I didn't consent *for / to* my details being used for marketing purposes.
7. Apparently, they're insisting *on / about* meeting us and discussing this in person.
8. All our operators are currently busy. We apologize *about / for* the inconvenience.

B Complete the sentences with the correct form of the verbs in the box and appropriate prepositions.

adhere	apologize	argue	complain	consent	deal	insist	thank you

1. I'd rather not ____________ this – if you give me my money, I'll say nothing more about it.
2. Did you ____________ them using your name?
3. I'm going to have to leave you to ____________ the problem if that's all right?
4. I ____________ an apology in writing.
5. If you don't ____________ the rules, you might lose your job.
6. You're always ____________ the conditions here, so why don't you leave?
7. I bought the flowers to ____________ your help.
8. Sam called me earlier to ____________ the misunderstanding.

VOCABULARY
Science; Advertising

A Complete the article with the correct form of the words in the box.

analysis data evidence finding researcher theory

No sugar, please

Sweeteners – replacements for sugar – are big business. The [1] ______________ is that, if we use products with no calories in place of sugar, we don't put on weight, while still enjoying the sweet taste we love. Saccharin, the original sweetener, was first used over 100 years ago. [2] ______________ thought they'd found something better in 1937. This was called cyclamate, and it enjoyed increasing popularity for several decades until further experiments were carried out on rats. The [3] ______________ from these experiments showed that the rats were developing cancer, and cyclamate was to blame. Next came aspartame, followed by sucralose, which was marketed as 'Splenda'.

However, there is a lot of [4] ______________ to suggest that we are not being very scientific in our approach to the problem. First, it is impossible to gather enough [5] ______________ until thousands of people have been exposed to untested (and potentially very harmful) chemicals. Moreover, recent [6] ______________ of the effect of these chemicals shows that they might have the opposite effect to the one that is intended – that is, they make us gain weight rather than lose it.

B Choose the correct options (a, b or c) to complete the sentences.

1 The idea of ____ loyalty is that customers are happy with a company so they keep buying their products.
   a target **b** consumer **c** brand
2 For music streaming services, the ____ market is the under-30s, with the exception of classical music, which is typically aimed at older people.
   a target **b** profile **c** brand
3 Popular, high-____ celebrities are the best people to get to advertise your product.
   a profile **b** brand **c** trend
4 Some people are paid a fortune to help identify what the next fashion ____ might be; manufacturers who can predict a new fashion have a great advantage.
   a campaign **b** trend **c** profile
5 We launched a massive advertising ____ on TV and radio, but sales were disappointingly low.
   a strategy **b** campaign **c** endorsement
6 People are just not buying our products – we need a new marketing ____.
   a trend **b** target **c** strategy
7 There have been a lot of complaints online – the manufacturer simply must listen to the demands of ____.
   a consumers **b** trends **c** targets
8 By getting a famous soccer player to ____ their product on TV, the company increased sales enormously.
   a profile **b** trend **c** endorse

GRAMMAR
Determiners and quantifiers

A **Match the beginnings of the sentences (1–6) to the endings (a–f).**

1 There were several ___
2 Make sure that each ___
3 Now let's go through any ___
4 The general manager and the chairman were away so neither ___
5 I've no doubt that some ___
6 I just think that's a large amount ___

a questions you'd like to ask.
b people there – probably five or six.
c of money to spend on a phone.
d people bought the product because they saw it advertised on TV.
e of them was at the meeting.
f person in the room gets a copy of this.

B **Choose the correct options to complete the sentences.**

1 John and Mark are interested in joining us – I spoke to *both* / *either* of them yesterday.
2 I didn't really buy much – just a *couple* / *few* things we needed around the house.
3 They say these two cell phones are the best, but I don't like *both* / *either* of them.
4 There's no need to spend any money – there are *plenty of* / *much to* free programs you can try.
5 Of all the people at the meeting, *no* / *none* of them were really paying attention.
6 *Every* / *Any* year, the company reviews its advertising strategy.
7 It's important to make sure there are *no* / *none* grammatical mistakes in your report.
8 Do you have *any* / *much* money you can lend me?

PRONUNCIATION
Connected speech: determiners and quantifiers

9.3 **A** **Listen to the sentences and draw a (‿) to show the connected speech in the words in bold.**

1 **A few of** the people in the room laughed.
2 **A large number of** people gathered outside the office.
3 There was **a great deal of** publicity for the new product.
4 **Plenty of** people came, but **none of them** bought anything.
5 **Some of** the customers were over 30, but **most of them** were much younger.
6 I spoke to **both of them**, but **neither of them** was interested.

9.4 **B** **Draw a (‿) to show the connected speech in the determiners and quantifiers below. Then listen and check.**

1 Thousands of people were sold faulty goods, but only half of them complained.
2 There are a whole bunch of reasons why I don't trust the brand – lack of quality being one of them.
3 Some of the best technology on sale these days is manufactured in China.
4 Most of the stores on Main Street have survived the recession.
5 A number of residents are worried the redevelopment will cause a great deal of disruption.

9.4 **C** **Listen again and repeat.**

READING

A Rank the following in terms of how effective you think they are in advertising.

___ celebrity endorsement
___ large public events
___ free giveaways
___ competitions
___ discounts/offers
___ statistics/data

B TOPIC SENTENCES Complete *Adapt or die: the challenge of advertising in the digital age* with the topic sentences (a–e).

- **a** Advertising evolved over the years from the simplistic messages displayed on posters and in newspapers to the sophisticated offerings of TV and radio.
- **b** Keeping your product 'fresh' and in the public eye is probably the most important thing you can do.
- **c** Sadly, these days, there's no escaping advertising.
- **d** Companies have always had a number of key objectives when advertising their products and services.
- **e** Television, which was once the most effective medium for advertising, has been pushed aside by the power of social and digital media platforms.

C READ FOR DETAIL Read the article again and answer the questions. Underline the parts of the text that give you the answers.

1. What four factors does the writer mention as being key objectives for businesses when advertising their products?
2. According to the article, why might a customer decide to try a different brand?
3. What does the writer say about consumers today compared with those of the past?
4. What does the writer say about 'admen' in the 1980s?
5. Which three new ways of watching shows does the writer mention?
6. Why is it important for companies that people talk about their campaigns?

D REFLECT Think about the answers to these questions.

1. What would cities look like without advertising (e.g. billboards, neon signs, etc)?
2. Overall, do you think advertising has a positive or negative effect on society as a whole? Why?

ADAPT OR DIE:

THE CHALLENGE OF ADVERTISING IN THE DIGITAL AGE

1___ Wherever you go and whatever you do, there's an image or a voice, or a jingle or slogan urging you to buy something. Billions are spent on advertising every year, but how effective is advertising, how important is it to businesses and how has it changed in the digital age?

2___ The first is obviously bigger sales and higher profits. To achieve this, companies need to let people know that they have something exciting to offer and they need to explain why it's better, or cheaper or more long-lasting than other similar products. For existing customers, who might be tempted to switch brands because their rivals have produced a newer version or a more impressive ad, businesses have to keep reminding them of the satisfaction they received from products in the past. It's also vital for companies to attract new customers: another key goal of advertising is to get people in the door which they do by using a combination of information and persuasion.

3___ Advertisers have also had to adapt to an increasingly knowledgeable audience, who is less easily fooled or impressed. At first, advertisements simply presented a product. Later, they made the product represent something positive, such as status or luxury – often by getting a celebrity to endorse it. Then creative teams, which included renowned movie directors, presented the public with artsy ads, funny ads or just plain weird ads. This explosion of 'creativity' occurred in the 1980s and admen were as much a feature of the cultural landscape as writers, artists and movie stars. Plenty of people today still remember TV ads from this period. Some of them have become part of popular culture.

4 ___ Digital media has changed everything. Many people today, especially the young, who are often the main target for advertisers, watch shows and get information from their phones and tablets. They are far more likely to record their favorite shows and skip through the ads or alternatively download or live-stream ad-free content. Now there are apps which can be used to stop ads popping up on our screens and many people are subscribing to pay-per-view platforms such as Netflix. In other words, we have reached a point where people are paying not to see ads. This trend means that advertisers are going to have to adapt again – as no doubt they will.

5 ___ It can be difficult to judge how successful an advertising campaign has been based on sales figures alone. Unless there has been a sudden and huge response to a particular ad, it isn't always possible to measure what effect the advertisement has had. But if sales figures are not an immediate measure of success, then perhaps a big response in the form of tweets and comments is? What businesses usually hope for with their advertising campaigns is to become part of the general conversational buzz, 'Have you seen the new ad for X? How about that polar bear, eh?' Whether the reaction is positive or negative – although obviously a positive reaction is preferred – then it keeps the brand in consumers' minds. And at the end of the day, that's what it's all about – which is why advertising, in all its changing forms, will continue to be vital to the business and commercial world.

Glossary

jingle (n) a short piece of music used to advertise a particular product

slogan (n) a short phrase that is easy to remember and is used to advertise something

LISTENING

A PREDICT You are going to listen to conversations in a recreation center and an office. In both conversations, one speaker is making a complaint. What might you complain about in these situations?

9.5 **B LISTEN FOR GIST** Listen to the conversations. What are the main issues discussed in each? Write notes.

9.5 **C FRONTING** Listen to the conversations again. Choose the correct options (a, b or c) to complete the sentences.

1 The customer is worried she'll miss her usual train at …
  - **a** 8:36.
  - **b** 8:54.
  - **c** 9:30.

2 She thought she would have the racquetball court for …
  - **a** 15 minutes.
  - **b** 25 minutes.
  - **c** 45 minutes.

3 The receptionist explains that after ten minutes …
  - **a** the facilities are made available to other customers.
  - **b** the customer is not allowed to use the facilities.
  - **c** the facilities are closed for the duration of the session.

4 He goes on to explain that Ms. Jackson will …
  - **a** be able to choose a new session at a different time.
  - **b** have to pay a cancellation fee.
  - **c** get a refund on her next booking.

5 Logan's boss asked him to print …
  - **a** 100 reports.
  - **b** 720 reports.
  - **c** 1,000 reports.

6 Logan didn't notice that the report …
  - **a** was missing an important word.
  - **b** contained a spelling mistake.
  - **c** gave an incorrect figure.

7 Logan's boss wishes that he would …
  - **a** read instructions properly.
  - **b** ask her if he's unsure about something.
  - **c** pay more attention to his work.

8 She didn't want Logan to seal the envelopes because she …
  - **a** wanted to check his work.
  - **b** had something to add to the report.
  - **c** made a mistake in the report.

D REFLECT Think about the answers to these questions.

1 Do you think the customer in the recreation center was right to be angry? Why/Why not?

2 How do you think Logan's boss should have dealt with the situation?

WRITING

A Read the proposal task and answer the questions.

> Your recreation center has been getting negative comments on its website and has been losing members. The manager has asked you to look at the complaints and to write a proposal for changes that can be made. You should include information about the problems people have mentioned and suggest ways to improve.

1 What is the current problem?

2 What recommendations do you need to make?

Proposal for improvements to the recreation center

1 ___

This proposal is intended to examine the complaints that have been made about the recreation center and suggest possible changes and improvements that could be made.

2 ___

Examination of the complaints reveals that they fall into two main categories. First, the standard of the equipment, some of which is considered to be outdated and occasionally faulty. 1***Consequently / Additionally***, there have been complaints that there simply aren't enough customer lockers. Second, the lack of sufficient numbers of instructors to oversee fitness sessions and show newcomers how to use the equipment. 2***Specifically / As a result*** of these issues, we are losing members. 3***Furthermore / Therefore***, the café has come under some minor criticism; 4***moreover / however***, I don't believe these are serious enough to concern management.

3 ___

It would be to the benefit of the recreation center if it invested in new equipment. 5***After all / In particular***, fitness is the main concern of the business and the equipment one of its main selling points. 6***Also / Owing to***, the center should recruit more experienced staff to attend fitness sessions and provide personal attention to members. Finally, it would be neither difficult nor expensive to increase the number of lockers and is something that can be dealt with quickly.

4 ___

Implementing the suggestions made above would result in an increase in members' satisfaction and fewer negative online complaints. 7***Therefore / Moreover***, this will lead to an improved public profile, attracting more members.

B Read the proposal and match the paragraphs (1–4) to the headings (a–d).

a Suggestions

b Final recommendations

c Current situation

d Introduction

C **USING DISCOURSE MARKERS** Read again and choose the correct options to complete the proposal.

WRITING PRACTICE

A **PREPARE** Read the proposal task below and write notes to answer the questions.

> You work in a department store near the center of town which is attracting fewer and fewer customers each year. Your manager has asked you to look into the problem and to write a proposal examining the causes of the problem and suggesting what action could be taken to improve the situation.

1 What reasons can you think of for the decrease in the number of shoppers?

2 What steps could be taken to attract more customers?

3 How could shopping at the department store be made into a more fun/interesting experience?

B **PLAN** Organize your notes from Exercise A into a plan for a proposal.

C **WRITE** Write your proposal in 150–250 words. Use your plan to help you.

D **EDIT** Edit your proposal. Check:

- spelling and punctuation
- use of headings
- use of formal discourse markers.

GRAMMAR
Reported speech

A Rewrite the sentences in reported speech.

1 'Can we turn the news off? It's so depressing.'
She asked me ______.

2 'My cousin works as a journalist for the local paper.'
She said ______.

3 'We can't make it. We'll be working then.'
Emily said ______.

4 He's been lying to us this whole time.'
Yuki thinks ______.

5 'This restaurant has gone downhill.'
He said ______.

6 'I saw that documentary last week.'
She said ______.

7 'Have you always been interested in current affairs?'
He asked me ______.

8 'I really must go, I have to work tomorrow.'
Liz said ______.

B Find and correct seven mistakes in the conversation.

Gary: So, how'd the interview go? Do you think you have enough for an article?

Jonas: Yeah, it was good. I'm hoping to focus on her background, so I asked her how did she get into acting.

Gary: Go on …

Jonas: Well, she said that she hasn't thought about being an actress at all. It was her parents that pushed her to do auditions.

Gary: So, she had pushy parents? That could be a good angle.

Jonas: Not exactly. She told me that she was working as a waitress back then, which she described as a 'dead-end job'. Anyway, her mom had heard that the local theater was holding auditions. She wasn't sure about it, but she told that her mom had persuaded her to go along.

Gary: Oh, so her parents were just supportive by the sounds of it. I guess she just passed the auditions and that was it?

Jonas: It was a little more interesting than that. She went to the auditions, but guess what?

Gary: What?

Jonas: She said that they'd been attending by none other than … Claudia Von Danke.

Gary: What, the Claudia Von Danke? You mean the Hollywood star?

Jonas: Crazy, huh?

Gary: Why was Von Danke at a local theater audition?

Jonas: Well, it turns out that Von Danke's cousin owns the company. She said that Von Danke told her she'd been the most promising actress that she came across in a long while. They exchanged numbers and barely a week later, she was off to Hollywood.

Gary: I can't believe this. I mean, this isn't common knowledge, right? I think we've hit on a great story here – 'local actress made it to Hollywood on the endorsement of Von Danke'.

Jonas: It gets better. She told me that she stops speaking to Von Danke. They've had a major falling out. She didn't say much, but I think there's a guy involved …

Gary: Right. Get me the number of Von Danke's agent. There is definitely a story here!

VOCABULARY
Traditional media

A Complete the blog post with the correct form of the words in the box.

biased coverage editor headline newspaper source subjective tabloid

MY LOVE OF NEWSPAPERS

Martin Harris I Oct. 10, 2019

I've always been into newspapers, ever since I started work as a paperboy when I was 12. Most of the papers I delivered around our town were [1] ________________, you know, the ones with a red top and all the gossip in them. They were the easiest to carry because they were so thin.

Some of the houses I delivered to had really long driveways, so I used to leave my bike at the gate and look through the paper as I walked up the path. In general, the tabloids are quite [2] ________________ toward one political position or another, although, to be honest, I wasn't really interested in all that back then. I mostly just read the [3] ________________ and the sports section.

Sunday was the hardest day to deliver papers. I only had to deliver ten [4] ________________ each day, but on a Sunday, they were huge! They were full of supplements and pull-out magazines – they had comprehensive [5] ________________ on pretty much every topic. The trouble was, they didn't fit in most normal mailboxes so I had to leave them on the doorstep. I got a lot of complaints!

When I finished school, I got a job reporting on sports for a local newspaper. The [6] ________________ was really supportive and took me under his wing. He taught me a lot about the industry, but I soon realized that being a journalist probably wasn't for me.

These days, I still read a paper every day, although I avoid some of them because the reporting seems to be so [7] ________________ – they're just not interested in presenting the facts. I don't read tabloid papers much anymore as they are full of pointless stories and sensationalism. Personally, I think they need to fact-check more, too, as some of the [8] ________________ for their stories seem unreliable. I do pick up a tabloid paper now and then when somebody leaves them on the train, but just for the sports sections!

B Choose the correct options to complete the sentences.

1 The word '*tabloid / broadsheet*' is often associated with poor-quality reporting.
2 The *source / headline* of a story is what a journalist needs to find.
3 The *manager / editor* is the person responsible for what goes in a newspaper.
4 *Tabloids / Broadsheets* are large-format newspapers with better-quality writing.
5 When a newspaper article is subjective or *biased / unbiased*, it reports only one side of a story.
6 The Sunday newspapers usually have good *supplements / coverage* of the week's events.
7 I don't read a paper every day, but I always glance at the *coverage / headlines*.

PRONUNCIATION
Avoiding interruption

A 10.1 Listen to this extract from the interview. What intonation is used on the underlined words – falling (↘) or rise-fall-rise (↗)? Why?

1 I don't think print media will be completely replaced, but it is certainly not driving the profits for most media companies.
2 Targeted marketing via social media is an interesting approach, but some consumers certainly see it as intrusive.
3 I understand why most papers are moving to a digital format, but I'm not sure some of the older readers will want to change.

B Read the sentences aloud. Try to use intonation to avoid interruption.

1 I don't think many young people read print newspapers anymore, because they get the majority of their news online.
2 There's little point in reading a newspaper that's biased because, apart from anything else, you're not getting the full story that way.
3 The only way to address the issue of fake news stories is for the government to better regulate social media.
4 Although there's been a shift in the way people find out about current events, that's not to say that print newspapers are dying.
5 The easiest way to stop the spread of stories that are inaccurate is stopping to think before we share information.

C 10.2 Listen to the sentences in Exercise B. Then practice saying them in the same way as the speakers do in the recording.

GRAMMAR

Reporting verbs

A Complete the article with the verbs in the box.

apologized convinced decided explained informed promised

Late-night intrusion

Twin Falls resident forgets keys and is mistaken for an intruder

Andrea Klopp | Tues. May 27th, 2019 | 2:58 pm MDT

On Tuesday night, Steven Frankel, of Austin Avenue, [1] ______________ police that someone was trying to break into his Twin Falls residence, after hearing suspicious noises on the roof. When officers arrived on the scene, they did indeed find a man on the roof. The man assured them that he had not gone there with the intent to steal and eventually [2] ______________ them of his innocence. The alleged intruder [3] ______________ that he lived in another townhouse in the same complex as Mr. Frankel. He said that he had [4] ______________ to go up on the roof to look at the stars because it was a nice night. However, he had locked himself out and he didn't have a phone with him. The noises had been him jumping up and down because he was cold. The man later [5] ______________ to the police and to his neighbor for the inconvenience and [6] ______________ to be more careful in future.

B Choose the correct options (a, b or c) to complete the sentences.

1 The police ___ leaving a spare key with a neighbor, not on the property.

a insist **b** recommend **c** remind

2 You can't ___ me for thinking the man was a burglar – what was he doing in my yard?

a blame **b** inform **c** threaten

3 After several hours of questioning, she ___ to committing the crime.

a agreed **b** confessed **c** confirmed

4 I ___ you not to go near that place – it's really dangerous!

a said **b** warned **c** insisted

5 She directly ___ him of stealing the money!

a accused **b** insisted **c** admitted

6 The manager ___ that we take a short break to get coffee.

a threatened **b** assured **c** suggested

7 The police officer ___ on questioning everyone a second time.

a apologized **b** insisted **c** regretted

8 The man ___ to upload the pictures unless he was paid $10,000.

a threatened **b** insisted **c** promised

VOCABULARY

Social media; Adjective + noun collocations

A Complete the sentences with the correct form of the words in the box.

campaign follow hashtag influence key factor meme reach trend viral wide audience

1 Anyone with around 3000 followers on Twitter and tweets about a specific industry is considered a micro-________________.

2 As successful YouTube vloggers, people often ask us how we make ________________ videos. Well, the ________________ is this: know your audience.

3 The government launched a ________________ to encourage people to be more aware of their online activities.

4 The popular ________________ has become a way for people to spread the campaign on social media.

5 I'm just not sure who you're trying ________________ with this ad? If you're looking for a ________________, then you might want to consider sharing it across different platforms.

6 You get the same type of things ________________ online toward the end of the year – Christmas ads, charity campaigns, etc.

7 If you're looking to get the word out about what your business is trying to do, it's probably worth trying to get more ________________ on Instagram and Twitter.

8 Someone circulated a funny ________________ with the company's president in it. It hasn't gone down well.

B Choose the correct options to complete the sentences.

1 Victor makes regular ***donations*** / ***mentions*** to support his favorite charities.

2 We need a better online presence if we want to reach a wider ***engagement*** / ***audience***.

3 The product simply won't sell without high ***content*** / ***engagement*** from the start.

4 I think the key ***factor*** / ***trend*** in our success was the care we take to produce less waste.

5 We should definitely try to include viral ***content*** / ***influencers*** in our advertising.

6 It started with just a few online ***mentions*** / ***hashtags***, but they were obviously read by the right people.

7 We expect a positive ***audience*** / ***reaction*** when we bring out the latest model next month.

8 Advertising on websites visited by young people helps us to reach our target ***audience*** / ***follows***.

PRONUNCIATION

Using intonation to attract and keep interest

10.3 **A Listen to the same sentences said in two different ways. Choose the sentences (a or b) that sound more engaging.**

1 Don't be afraid of using traditional media as well as digital media in your advertising. *a* / *b*

2 The campaign started off small but grew to capture the world's attention. *a* / *b*

3 The meme was seen a million times by people all over the world. *a* / *b*

4 The brainchild of a bored student soon became a multimillion-dollar industry. *a* / *b*

5 Your profit will only increase when you have a better understanding of your target audience. *a* / *b*

6 Bad publicity can quickly undo even the best marketing campaigns. *a* / *b*

10.4 **B Listen and repeat the sentences. Try to copy the stress, intonation and pauses that each speaker uses.**

1 There are plenty of blogs out there with good content. They just need good marketing to help them thrive.

2 It doesn't matter what your business is. These days, no one can afford to ignore social media marketing.

3 There is only one key rule to follow on Twitter – that's hashtag, hashtag, hashtag.

4 If you want your content to reach a wider audience, you should consider working on search engine optimization.

5 It can take around three months for a blog post to be indexed on Google. Don't sit around waiting to see if your content will be popular – spend that time writing more!

READING

A PREDICT Look at the title of the article and answer the questions.

1 What do you think radio has to offer that other forms of media don't?

2 Have music streaming platforms made the radio redundant?

3 Are news broadcasts on radio more or less reliable than on other media?

B READ FOR DETAIL Read *Does radio have a place in the digital age?* and answer the questions.

1 What role did radio use to play in traditional households?

2 What does the writer think the statistic for daily listeners would be?

3 What comparison does the writer make between the radio and print media?

4 How has radio adapted to the digital age?

5 According to the writer, what five qualities attract listeners to the radio?

C SUBSTITUTION Read the article again. Match the words in bold (1–5) to the ideas they refer to (a–e).

a of the qualities ___

b broadcasting live / intimacy ___

c listen to the radio ___

d listeners ___

e radio ___

D REFLECT Think about the answers to these questions.

1 Do you think live broadcasting, on the radio or TV, still has a place in modern society? Why/Why not?

2 Which forms of media do you think may die out over the next decade? Why?

Does radio have a place in the digital age?

There was a time when the radio was at the heart of the living room. Families would gather around the polished walnut cabinet to listen to everything from the news headlines to the latest jazz records. But is there still a place for the radio in the age of podcasts and Spotify? Does anyone still listen to the radio?

Well, as it turns out, many of us [1]**do**. According to a recent survey, 89% of respondents said they listen to the radio at least once a week. I imagine a similar percentage tune in every day. Some listen while they're doing the housework, others use the [2]**one** in their car. Builders sing along to stereos as they work. We listen to music, interviews, weather forecasts, traffic updates – the list just goes on and on. Yet since the dawn of television, people have been saying that the age of radio is over, just as they have long said that print is dead.

Like all other media, radio has had to adapt – and fast – to the digital revolution. For example, most mainstream radio broadcasts are available online and many programs can now be downloaded. The move online has allowed traditional broadcasters to reach a wider audience, yet I'd argue it is some of the qualities that radio has had from the start that has sustained its popularity. [3]**One** is that it is far more intimate than other media. We listen so regularly that the presenters have become familiar to us – we trust their judgement and taste. We also see them as reliable sources of information – a rare quality in the era of fake news. Many of the programs are also broadcast live, which makes us feel more involved in the discussion.

Another aspect of [4]**this** is that radio can be just as interactive as social media, if not more so. Listeners can call in, tweet or text, joining the conversation with politicians, movie stars, musicians and celebrities. In fact, I'm sure for [5]**some** this is one of its big attractions. Radio also has a wider reach in the moment than other media; it can be local, national or international. You can tune in to the latest news from your home town, what your Governor or President is up to or a baseball game in the Domincan Repbublic. What's more, with the arrival of digital radio, not only is sound quality hugely improved, but listeners can also use the LCD screen to receive information about what song's currently playing, phone numbers for the ads they're listening to, album art and much more. And if you take a look at just a single day's listing of programs, you'll be surprised at how much more radio has to offer.

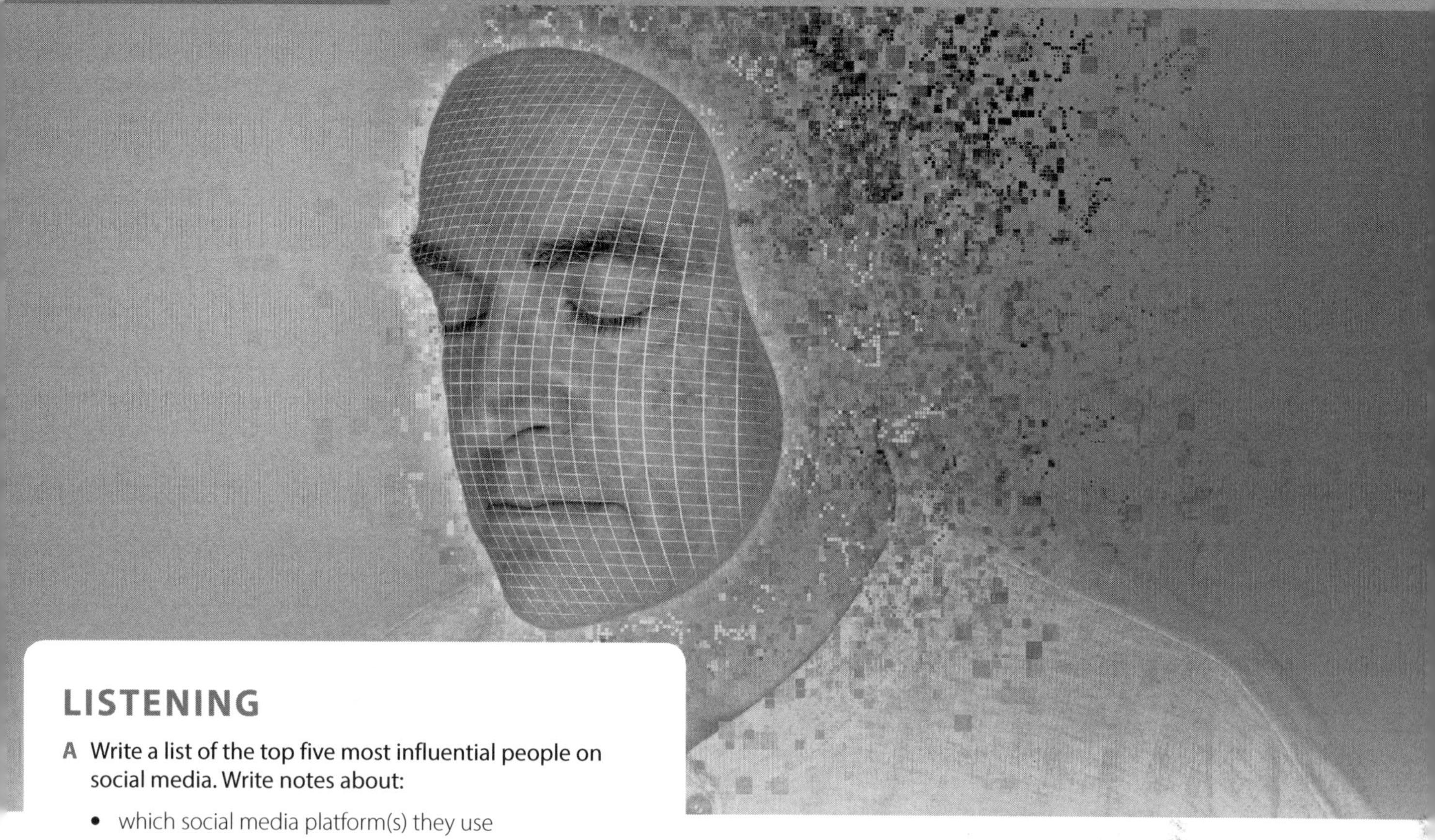

LISTENING

A Write a list of the top five most influential people on social media. Write notes about:

- which social media platform(s) they use
- the kind of content they produce
- why you think they're so influential.

B **LISTEN FOR GIST** Listen to the first part of a talk about a social media influencer. What is unique about her?
10.5

C **LISTEN FOR MAIN IDEAS** Listen to the full talk. Choose the correct options (a, b or c) to complete the sentences.
10.6

1 The speaker believes that social media …
  a is too addictive for teenagers.
  b makes her daughter unhappy.
  c makes us question what's 'real'.

2 Lil Miquela is an influencer who has …
  a criticized the fashion industry.
  b struggled to gain followers.
  c divided public opinion.

3 The speaker says she is surprised that Lil Miquela …
  a has been used as part of a marketing campaign.
  b has caused such a strong reaction online.
  c has been branded by some commenters as 'fake'.

4 The speaker argues that, like Lil Miquela, we all use social media to present …
  a our true selves.
  b the best version of ourselves.
  c multiple versions of ourselves.

5 The speaker concludes that we should …
  a stop listening to social media influencers.
  b share more of our everyday lives online.
  c accept that we're different from social media influencers.

Glossary

influencer (n) someone whose actions on social media change or affect the way others behave
persona (n) the way your character appears to others
vlogger (n) a person who makes videos and posts them on the internet

D **LISTEN FOR REPAIR AND ELABORATION** Listen to the full talk again. Are these sentences true (T) or false (F)? Correct the false sentences.
10.6

1 Lil Miquela's Instagram account currently has one million followers. **T / F**
2 The speaker says Lil Miquela behaves just like every other influencer. **T / F**
3 Traditional media outlets were unaware of the debate surrounding Lil Miquela. **T / F**
4 The speaker argues that Lil Miquela has made us redefine what's 'real' online. **T / F**
5 The speaker thinks everyone knows beauty vloggers present an enhanced version of themselves. **T / F**

E **REFLECT** Think about the answers to these questions.

1 Do you agree with the speaker that Lil Miquela is 'no less real' than human influencers? Why/Why not?
2 How else is social media changing the way we think about reality?
3 Do you think online celebrities have too much influence over the way we behave?

WRITING

A Read the essay prompt and answer the questions.

> Since the invention of e-readers, people have disagreed over which provides the better reading experience – e-books or conventional, printed books. Discuss both views and give your opinion.

1 What are the two points of view you need to discuss?
2 What else do you need to do?

B Read the essay and choose the best summary of the writer's argument (a, b or c).

a Buying an e-book reader has changed the writer's opinion of printed books.
b Despite their many advantages, the writer will never switch to e-books.
c The writer prefers printed books but argues both forms have their place.

Some years ago, people were announcing the death of the printed book. The e-reader was the future: portable, practical, a whole library in your pocket. [1] ______________ I own one myself, I believe it is far too early to mourn the death of the print book.

The advantages of e-readers are fairly obvious. They are easy to carry, can be read in most light conditions and have features to help those with eyesight problems. If you are an avid reader going on vacation, you don't want to add weight to your luggage in the form of books. They can also save you money – once you have an e-reader, books are cheaper and quicker to buy. [2] ______________, these advantages are not enough to make me give up print books.

[3] ______________ print book lovers like me may agree that these developments are not a bad thing, they [4] ______________ feel that there's no substitute for the real thing. Good jacket design makes books into objects of beauty in themselves and holding a digital machine in your hands cannot replace the feel of a real book. And, [5] ______________ e-readers make for easy reading, print books are less of a strain on the eyes. Besides, don't we already spend a lot of the time staring at screens?

On balance, there's no reason why they can't live side by side. You can take your e-reader on the commute to work and read the print version of *War and Peace* in your armchair at home.

C Scan the essay again. Put the following in order to show the essay structure.

___ giving a personal opinion
___ outlining the disadvantages of e-readers
___ paraphrasing the essay question
___ outlining the advantages of e-readers

D CONCESSION Complete the essay with words and phrases of concession in the box.

although as much as however nevertheless while

WRITING PRACTICE

A PREPARE Read the essay prompt and use the questions below to help you write notes.

> Some people argue that communication via digital media is having a negative impact on young people's knowledge of the basics of written language. Others argue the new vocabulary used on social media is enriching the English language. Discuss both views and give your opinion.

1 What are some of the differences between the conventional written language and the language used on social media (e.g. acronyms like FOMO and ROFL, slang, grammar, spelling, use of emojis, etc)?
2 Does this necessarily mean that young people will write school essays in the same way? Why/Why not?

B PLAN Organize your notes from Exercise A into a plan for a persuasive essay.

C WRITE Write your essay in 150–250 words. Use your plan to help you.

D EDIT Edit your essay. Check:

- spelling and punctuation
- use of phrases of concession
- an appropriate structure/tone has been used.

Irregular Verbs

Base form	Simple past	Past participle
be	was/were	been
become	became	become
begin	began	begun
break	broke	broken
bring	brought	brought
build	built	built
buy	bought	bought
can	could	been able to
catch	caught	caught
choose	chose	chosen
come	came	come
cost	cost	cost
cut	cut	cut
drink	drank	drunk
eat	ate	eaten
fall	fell	fallen
feel	felt	felt
find	found	found
forget	forgot	forgotten
get	got	got
give	gave	given
go	went	gone/been
grow	grew	grown
have	had	had
hear	heard	heard
hit	hit	hit
hold	held	held
hurt	hurt	hurt
keep	kept	kept
know	knew	known
leave	left	left
lend	lent	lent
let	let	let

Base form	Simple past	Past participle
lose	lost	lost
make	made	made
mean	meant	meant
meet	met	met
must	had to	had to
pay	paid	paid
put	put	put
read	read	read
ride	rode	ridden
run	ran	run
say	said	said
see	saw	seen
sell	sold	sold
send	sent	sent
set	set	set
shut	shut	shut
sing	sang	sung
sit	sat	sat
sleep	slept	slept
speak	spoke	spoken
spell	spelled	spelled
spend	spent	spent
stand	stood	stood
steal	stole	stolen
take	took	taken
teach	taught	taught
tell	told	told
think	thought	thought
throw	threw	thrown
understand	understood	understood
wear	wore	worn
win	won	won
write	wrote	written

PHONETIC SYMBOLS

Single vowels			Diphthongs			Consonants					
/ɪ/	fish	/fɪʃ/	/uw/	news	/nuw/	/p/	pen	/pen/	/s/	snake	/sneɪk/
/iː/	bean	/biːn/	/eɪ/	face	/feɪs/	/b/	bag	/bæg/	/z/	zoo	/zuː/
/ʊ/	foot	/fʊt/	/ɔɪ/	boy	/bɔɪ/	/t/	tea	/tiː/	/ʃ/	shop	/ʃɒp/
/uː/	shoe	/ʃuː/	/oʊ/	nose	/noʊz/	/d/	dog	/dɒg/	/ʒ/	television	/ˈtelɪvɪʒən/
/e/	egg	/eg/	/ju/	use	/juz/	/ʧ/	chip	/ʧɪp/	/m/	map	/mæp/
/ə/	mother	/ˈmʌðər/	/aɪ/	eye	/aɪ/	/ʤ/	jazz	/ʤæz/	/n/	name	/neɪm/
/ɜː/	word	/wɜːrd/	/aʊ/	mouth	/maʊθ/	/k/	cake	/keɪk/	/ŋ/	ring	/rɪŋ/
/ɔː/	talk	/tɔːk/				/g/	girl	/gɜːrl/	/h/	house	/haʊs/
/æ/	back	/bæk/				/f/	film	/fɪlm/	/l/	leg	/leg/
/ʌ/	bus	/bʌs/				/v/	verb	/vɜːrb/	/r/	road	/roʊd/
/ɑː/	arm	/ɑːrm/				/θ/	thing	/θɪŋ/	/w/	want	/wɒnt/
/ɒ/	top	/tɒp/				/ð/	these	/ðiːz/	/j/	yes	/jes/

UNIT 6

Lesson 6.4, Listening, Exercise B
6.6 **A = Anya C = Cleo**

A: Cleo! I was so happy when I got your message. I haven't seen you in ages! How are you? Are you still living in Philadelphia?

C: It's so great to see you, too, Anya! Yes, I am. I'm married now and I have two children.

A: That's fantastic! Girls, boys? How old are they?

C: My daughter's 6 and my son's 12.

A: 12? That's amazing! How's he doing in school? It's not so bad at that age, is it? It's when they're 15 or 16 that things start to get a bit tough – a lot of pressure …

C: Well, the thing is, Anya …

A: … what with exams and so on. I know my daughter finds it quite stressful. She's about to take her exams and, well, she has a lot on her plate. Still, it's worth it, in the end, isn't it? I mean, to improve their job prospects.

C: Actually, neither of my children go to school.

A: Seriously?

C: Yes, my husband and I homeschool both our children.

A: You're joking, right? I mean, how will they get the certifcations they need to go to college?

C: Just because they're homeschooled doesn't mean they're not getting an education, Anya. My husband teaches them math and science, and I teach them English literature and essay writing.

A: Look – I know you studied English Lit, and your husband is a biologist, but, I mean, those aren't the only subjects. What about music, art, geography and, well, everything? Don't you think you've bitten off a little more than you can chew? It's a huge responsibility. How can you provide them with a full curriculum?

C: We hire tutors for those subjects which we can't teach ourselves, and, as a matter of fact, the kids are getting better grades than some of their peers who go to mainstream schools. They're not required to study subjects they don't like and they do really well in the ones they love. What you don't understand is that they have so many more choices. They're not limited by a rigid school curriculum. They can think outside the box. We go on nature walks and visit art galleries. We do craft projects and experiments. There's so much more flexibility with, well, with the way we do things.

A: You still haven't explained how you expect them to get into a good college, Cleo.

C: College isn't everybody's cup of tea. There are other paths in life. Actually, my son wants to set up his own business when he's older. Some of America's most successful businesspeople didn't go to college.

A: Well, I guess that's true but, what about friends? I mean, one of the main reasons we send our children to school is to learn to socialize. How do you expect them to … to … learn to deal with the real world? You can't keep them hidden away at home forever!

C: I'm sorry, but that's ridiculous. I'm not keeping them 'hidden at home'. As a matter of fact, my son is quite shy, and he found it difficult to cope when he first started high school. That's why we pulled him out.

A: Oh, come on! You're not helping him to deal with his shyness with your overprotection. He has to learn to deal with difficult people and situations. You're depriving him of the skills he'll need in his adult life.

C: Well, I for one think that the school environment doesn't prepare you for adult life. Children don't always treat each other well, you know. Quite the opposite in fact. I'm sorry, but you seem to have a very negative attitude.

A: Look, I'm sorry, Cleo, we seem to have gotten off on the wrong foot. Let's just forget this whole topic of conversation and start again. Umm ... How are your parents?

C: They're fine, thank you. Look, Anya, it's been nice talking to you, but I have to go. I'll … maybe I'll see you sometime. Bye.

A: But ... Cleo!

UNIT 7

Lesson 7.4, Listening, Exercise A
7.5 **L = Lecturer**

L: When I was here five years ago, I spoke about the need for society to find creative ways to address the issue of overcrowding in our towns and cities. I wanted to inspire people to make better use of the space we have and many projects since – for example, the revitalization work happening in neigborhoods near Los Angeles – seem to have taken my lead.

However, space in urban areas is still at a premium. Today's megacities continue to expand at an alarming rate and many experts believe that by 2050, two-thirds of the world's population will be living in urban areas. For generations now, architects have carved out space by building upward. Now, it seems, some city leaders have decided the answer to our problems may lie below ground, and I hope that the projects I'm going to show you today will make you feel the same.

Lesson 7.4, Listening, Exercise B
7.6 **L = Lecturer**

L: A great example of how the space below cities can be exploited is the 'Growing Underground' project in the UK. This is London's first and only underground farm – created in old underground tunnels which run 30 meters beneath ground level. The farm is accessed via a London subway station, and if you brave the 129 steps deep into the darkness, you are rewarded with an astonishing sight – rows and rows of perfect green vegetables and herbs packed into clinical white shelving units.

The farm uses specially designed lighting and watering systems – in fact, it actually uses 70% less water than conventional agricultural methods and 50% less energy. Unlike a regular greenhouse above ground, no extra heat or light is required during the winter months and the temperature in the underground garden is kept at a steady 16 degrees Celsius. And, as it is literally under its customers' feet, delivering the produce to the market and restaurants which it supplies causes very little pollution in terms of transportation.

And you know what? There are eight huge shelters just like this one spread across the city, just waiting for entrepreneurs like Richard Ballard and Steven Dring – the creators of Growing Underground – to bring them to life.

Equally intriguing is SubTropolis, an underground business complex in Kansas City. Like many areas in the American Midwest, it was once known for its booming industry, but over the past three decades, that has all changed. When the once-successful mining operations in Kansas closed in the 1940s, they left behind huge networks of caves and tunnels – massive, empty space without use or purpose. Twenty years later, the largest mine was bought by a local entrepreneur and converted into a sprawling complex of underground offices and commercial premises known as SubTropolis.

Today, more than 1,500 people work there in a variety of businesses. Interestingly, the US Postal Service also stores two billion dollars'-worth of postage stamps in the facility! Like Growing Underground, the network of tunnels here maintains a constant temperature of between 18 and 21 degrees Celsius, so the whole complex uses very little energy, and businesses are able to save thousands of dollars on energy bills. It is also considered to be a very secure location for businesses as access to the site is limited. Food distributors find the site extremely useful because the constant temperature and humidity levels are ideal for storing products such as cheese, coffee and wine.

But it's not just commercial operations that can benefit from building below ground. In Amsterdam, bicycles are a hugely popular means of transportation. This is obviously great for the environment, but bikes take up space, and it's becoming increasingly difficult for the thousands of people that ride bikes in the city to find somewhere to park. To address this, the city has recently constructed a huge underground bike park. Offering up to 3000 spaces for both local residents and tourists, the new facility is situated underneath one of Amsterdam's main train stations, making it ideal for anyone that needs to continue their journey by train. It also offers riders protection from vandalism and theft – both of which have become a serious problem in the city in recent years.

For me, all of these projects represent a creative way forward for our cities. Since the last time I spoke on this stage, overcrowding has arguably become one of the biggest threats to our society. If we continue building without thought to the millions of people that want to live and work in our cities, I'd argue that our way of life is under serious threat. It's only with innovative solutions, like the ones I've discussed today, that we can tackle the very real problems of urban development. Thank you.

UNIT 8

Lesson 8.4, Listening, Exercise B

8.5 P = Presenter J = Jo

P: Hello and welcome to *The Book Group*. This week, we're talking about crime fiction, which recently became the best-selling genre in the US for the first time ever. In fact, over the past three years, sales of crime fiction have risen by an incredible 19%, meaning that one in every three books sold in the US is about crime. So, what is it that draws people to these stories of murder and violence? Here to help us answer that question is Jo Craig, best-selling author of *Without an Alibi* and creator of the ever-popular Billy Chandler detective series. Jo – welcome to the show.

J: Thanks for having me, I'm always happy to talk about books.

P: Well, you're in the right place. So, Jo – why do you think we love crime writing so much?

J: Well, first of all, most crime novels tend to follow a fairly well-worn path: an unexplained murder is followed by a complicated trail of detection and discovery, led by an engaging central character. He or she might be a professional police officer – like the Swedish Kurt Wallander or, of course, my own character, Billy Chandler. Or they might just be a normal person who takes a lively interest in crime – like Agatha Christie's unlikely amateur detective, Miss Marple.

P: These creations are often a bit different from a regular police officer, though, aren't they?

J: Absolutely! The central character typically has unusual personal habits or quirks: Sherlock Holmes plays the violin and Adam Dalgliesh writes poetry.

P: So, is crime writing just about following the same old formula?

J: Well, good writers do also use the genre as a means to explore wider social themes such as poverty, race relations or gender roles. However, with a few exceptions, the genre doesn't experiment – what you see, or read in the cover blurb, is what you get. And in my view, that is what most readers are looking for and expect – a gripping plot which is guaranteed to keep them entertained for the few hours or days it will take them to read the book. Having said that, there are other factors which may contribute to the readers' interest in murder and the strange twists of the human mind.

P: Such as?

J: Well, in real life, we often see people, or groups of people, that we consider to be naturally 'bad', getting away with actions which we believe are immoral. From unjust or unfair situations in our everyday lives to serious crimes which affect the lives of thousands. Many of us – in a complicated, mixed-up, stressful world – would like to see a simpler reality in which good triumphs over evil, reason over senselessness. Rarely do we witness 'good' winning out over 'evil' in real life, but the crime novel allows people to reverse that trend – even if it's only in our imaginations.

P: So, it gives readers the chance to see bad people pay for their actions?

J: Exactly. It actually reminds me of one of the characters in Oscar Wilde's *The Importance of Being Earnest* who says, 'The good end happily, and the bad unhappily. That is what fiction means.' I think that's certainly what we expect from the crime novels we read. I would also argue that the messiness of ordinary life is something which drives us to reach for the murder mystery. We can never predict what's going to happen in our own lives: work, family, relationships, poor health – all of these can make day-to-day living a tough proposition.

P: So, why would people want to read about something depressing, too? Wouldn't they try to find something more uplifting or positive?

J: Well, crime fiction always solves a complicated web of events. By the time you turn over the last page, you've been given answers to all the puzzles which were posed while you were reading the book. Rarely are we given such an opportunity in our own lives, and maybe that's what we find comfort in – a puzzle whose pieces all fit neatly into place in the end. It has also been observed that readers' appetite for crime fiction increases in times of economic hardship. This would seem to reinforce the idea that people look for certainty in times of difficulty: human courage and patience winning out in a difficult world.

P: If only that were so in real life!

J: Yes, exactly!

UNIT 9

Lesson 9.4, Listening, Exercise B

9.5 **N = Narrator R = Receptionist H = Helen F = Flora L = Logan**

Conversation 1

R: Good morning. Welcome to Ann Arbor Recreation Center! How are you today?

H: Not very well, actually.

R: Oh, I'm sorry to hear that. How can I help?

H: Well, I booked a racquetball court for seven o'clock and somebody else is using it!

R: Oh, really? That's odd. Let me take a look at this morning's reservations. OK. Can I have your name, please?

H: It's Helen. Helen Jackson. Listen, is this going to take long? This really is going to upset my schedule. I'm already running at least ten minutes late. The 8:36 – that's the train I usually catch to work – will be leaving soon. At this rate, I'll be lucky to get the one at 8:54. Either way, I'd be lucky to make it into work by 9:30 and, frankly, it'll be all your fault!

R: I really am terribly sorry to have held you up Ms. Jackson, but if you'll just give me a minute to check. It shouldn't take too long.

H: Frankly, it's already taken too long. A single, 45-minute session is what I booked. I received a confirmation email about it last week.

R: OK, so it says here that you reserved the court for seven o'clock and it's now seven fifteen.

H: And?

R: Ten minutes is all we allow for late arrivals, I'm afraid. Anyone more than ten minutes late may lose their reservation to a walk-in customer. It's company policy, I'm afraid.

H: Ridiculous is what it is. There was nothing about this policy in my confirmation email.

R: Actually, it's clearly stated in the terms and conditions at the bottom.

H: I see. Well, that doesn't help me now. I expect a full refund.

R: Uh, I'm afraid we cannot offer refunds to customers that missed their sessions.

H: This is absurd!

R: We can, however, book another session for tomorrow morning. Maybe you can make it in for seven this time?

Conversation 2

F: Morning, Logan. Please sit down. I take it you got my note?

L: Yep – all done. There was a little problem, though.

F: Oh, really? What was that?

L: Well, the photocopier ran out of paper, so I was only able to print 720 copies of the report.

F: 720? 100 copies is what I asked you to print, Logan. One for each person attending the presentation.

L: Wait, what? But … but … I thought … I'm sure the note said 1,000 copies.

F: A thousand copies would be ridiculous, Logan. Never mind, at least we have enough for the presentation. I take it you did check the spelling as I asked?

L: Of course, boss. Look …

F: '*Diamond Electrical Services* wishes to thank you for your customer loyalty over the last 12 moths.' Moths, Logan?

L: Uh, that's right.

F: Months is what it's supposed to say, Logan. Not moths! Every single one of these reports will now have to be thrown away.

L: I … I … I'm really sorry. I guess I just didn't …

F: ... didn't what, Logan? Think for two minutes? Why you don't take more care with your work, that's what I don't understand. Just give me the pile of envelopes. I'll take the reports out and redo them.

L: Um, how are we going to take the reports out? I mean the envelopes are all sealed.

F: Sealed, Logan? Sealed? I specifically wrote, 'Do not seal the envelopes' in my note. I wanted to check everything first, because, frankly, I thought you might make a mistake and, sadly, I was right.

L: I … I don't know what to say.

F: It's fine, Logan. Just go and find some more paper for the photocopier, will you?

UNIT 10

Lesson 10.4, Listening, Exercise C

10.6 **L = Lecturer**

L: Thank you. Now, I'd like to start by telling you a little bit about my daughter. She, like most teenagers in this day and age, is completely addicted to social media. It's where she gets her news, how she connects with her friends, what she turns to for advice. And for the most part, I'm fine with this. It's not my thing, but as long as she's happy, I'm happy. But what does interest me is the ability of social media to shape our view of reality. In fact, I'd argue that in recent years, social media has blurred the lines between what's real and what's fake.

Let me give you an example. One of the latest influencers taking the fashion world by storm is 19-year-old model, Miquela Sousa. Better known as Lil Miquela, her profile first appeared on Instagram in 2016 and has since gained well over a million followers. 1.5 million to be precise. This success landed her a contract with the fashion house Prada and she is now the face of their 3D-generated advertising campaign.

Her Instagram account itself is fairly typical for someone of her age – endless selfies of her modeling trendy streetwear or posing with celebrities. She's also fairly outspoken on current affairs, is regularly involved in fundraising campaigns and has a burgeoning music career. In other words, she does everything that other influencers do.

Yet, her rise to fame has caused a media storm. People are outraged and have expressed their anger in no uncertain terms online. Why? Because Lil Miquela is not real – that is to say, not flesh and blood real. She's the world's first 'virtual influencer' and was created as part of a digital art project by Sara Decou and Trevor McFedries.

What I think is most astonishing about all of this is not that someone would choose to create a virtual persona like this – it actually makes sense from a marketing point of view – but that people would react so passionately to her very existence. When she first appeared on the scene, furious debates erupted on social media – a story that was actually picked up by mainstream news outlets – with some commenters, often in the most unpleasant or abusive language, branding her as fake. Others, with equal relish, leapt to her defense. She seems to arouse as much feeling as a living, breathing person. For me, this just goes to show how much social media has distorted our view of reality. What I mean is – her very existence seems to have made us question what we mean by 'real' when it comes to online content.

But is Lil Miquela really so different from the rest of us? Don't we all use Instagram pages, blogs, YouTube channels and Twitter feeds to present an idealized version of ourselves, not necessarily who we are? I mean, seriously, does anybody really believe that those beauty vloggers actually look like that in real life? The right lighting, the best digital equipment, clever make-up tricks and editing can make anybody look like a model of perfection – an image utterly unrelated to the real, living, breathing person. What I'm saying is – our online persona often bears very little resemblance to our real self.

And for me, this is where the dilemma lies. I'm happy for my daughter to take inspiration from the people she follows online, to aspire to a different lifestyle. But are influencers setting an impossibly high bar? They seem to have the perfect life. But is this because they don't actually share the boring parts? You don't get likes or retweets for pictures of you locking the front door or taking the trash out. You're expected to present the best version of yourself – the one that goes on glamorous vacations and eats in expensive restaurants. But most of us aren't celebrities, and sometimes our lives aren't all that great. And surely, that's OK, too. What I'm trying to say is that in a world where the difference between 'real' and 'fake' is almost impossible to distinguish, perhaps it's more important than ever to teach our children it's OK to be themselves.

Answer key

6.1 The right method?

GRAMMAR

A

1 b **2** a **3** b **4** c **5** c **6** a **7** b **8** a

B

1 aren't / are not allowed to talk
2 should learn
3 let me deal with
4 must not tell anyone
5 we obliged to stay
6 don't have to add
7 am supposed to study
8 aren't / are not obliged

PRONUNCIATION

A

rise-fall

B

1, 4, 5, 6

VOCABULARY

A

1 f **2** d **3** e **4** b **5** a **6** c

B

1 scholarship
2 secondary
3 campus
4 lectures
5 lectures
6 seminars
7 graduate
8 vocational

6.2 Traditions of youth

GRAMMAR

A

1 the **2** the **3** a **4** an **5** – **6** – **7** a **8** the

B

1 an; the
2 the; –
3 the; the
4 –; a
5 a; the
6 –; –
7 the; the
8 the; the

C

… coming-of-age traditions around ~~a~~ **the** world …; The Sateré-Mawé tribe live deep in ~~an~~ **the** Amazon rainforest …; … to search for ~~the~~ **a** specific species of ant …; … which can cause ~~the~~ extreme pain …; Once the boys find ~~an~~ **the** ants …; … was enough of ~~a~~ **an** initiation …; Each boy has to wear **the** glove for …; ~~A~~ **The** initiation can last months …; … being stung by **a** bullet ant would probably …; … part of the transition to ~~the~~ manhood.

PRONUNCIATION

B

1 The‿ants have a venomous sting.
2 The‿age-old tradition of land diving
3 The second Monday‿of January‿is a special day‿in Japan.
4 These young adults then go on to celebrate at parties in the‿evening.
5 It's a coming-of-age movie‿about three young friends growing up together.
6 I‿often wonder what it would be like to be‿in the Sateré-Mawé tribe and do the‿initiation!

VOCABULARY

A

1 well-known
2 old-fashioned
3 last-minute
4 up-to-date
5 thrill-seeking
6 high-risk
7 seven-bedroom
8 organically grown

B

1 two-hour
2 100-mile
3 well-behaved
4 world-famous
5 never-ending
6 Spanish-speaking

C

1 made
2 Making
3 did
4 making
5 do
6 doing
7 making
8 do

6.3 Reading

READING

C

1 them (my school days)
2 we (boys)
3 them/which (traditions / physical tests)
4 they (the boys)
5 it (paddling students / corporal punishment)
6 that (worsted wool)

D

1 NG (There's nothing in the text to indicate which school James went to)
2 NG (The writer says that the parents believed this, but not that this was necessarily true)

3 NG (The writer doesn't give his own opinion, but says '… that you might consider barbaric.')
4 F (It was banned in state schools in 1986, but '… continued in schools like mine for another decade before being outlawed')
5 T
6 T

6.4 Listening

LISTENING

C

1 a 2 b 3 b 4 c 5 a

D

1 F (She uses 'a lot on her plate' to mean that her daughter is very busy right now.)
2 T
3 T
4 F (She says that 'College isn't everybody's cup of tea', meaning that it doesn't work for everyone.)
5 T

6.5 Write a report

WRITING

B

Education and law have seen the greatest decline; the two most popular subjects are computer science and pre-clinical medicine.

C

1 c 2 e 3 d 4 a 5 f 6 b

WRITING PRACTICE

C

Model answer

<u>Gender gap in higher education choices</u>

Introduction

This report evaluates the results of a survey on gender differences in certain college subjects and suggests ways of closing this gap.

Results

The key trend indicated by the chart is that there is a divide between arts subjects and the 'hard' sciences which is closely linked to gender. Most students studying computer science are male. Males also make up a far greater proportion of those studying mathematical sciences and engineering and technology.

In contrast, female students dominate the arts and 'soft' sciences, e.g. creative arts and design and social studies. More than twice as many female students study languages as males.

Interpretation

It is evident that as things stand, male students are drawn to the sciences, while female students opt for the arts. No doubt, gender stereotyping plays some part, yet studies show that female students equal or outperform male students in science, technology and math coursework but do less well on tests. The idea that certain subjects are masculine or feminine still affects some people. That, and lack of confidence and support, has an impact on students' choice of subjects.

Conclusion

I would recommend that schools provide encouragement and support for female students who want to study sciences and discourage gender stereotyping. Similarly, more male students should be persuaded that arts subjects are neither feminine nor without future practical use.

7.1 Open spaces

GRAMMAR

A

1 b 2 a 3 c 4 a 5 c 6 b 7 b 8 b

B

1 'd/would have given
2 'd buy
3 wouldn't be
4 had
5 would have gone
6 didn't have to

C

1 had not / hadn't taken
2 would not / wouldn't have
3 had not / hadn't fought
4 might not have
5 would make
6 had
7 would go
8 achieve

VOCABULARY

A

1 c 2 b 3 c 4 a 5 c 6 b

B

1 to restore
2 constructed
3 demolished
4 transformed
5 to relocate
6 extended

PRONUNCIATION

A

1 b 2 b 3 b 4 a 5 b 6 a

7.2 Make a change

GRAMMAR

A

I wish ~~I've~~ **I'd** done things a little …; If only I**'d** tried a little bit harder …; If only I ~~do~~ **did** a job that I …; … I wish people ~~won't~~ **wouldn't** ask me what I …; I also sometimes wish ~~I've~~ **I'd** been braver …; If only I ~~would have~~ **had had** the courage to try …

B

1 b 2 a 3 c 4 a 5 b 6 b 7 c 8 a

VOCABULARY

A

1 get around to **2** run out of **3** come up against
4 look up to **5** come up with **6** keep up with
7 get along with **8** cut down on

B

1 sharing **2** pollution **3** spirit **4** party **5** banks
6 group **7** workers **8** exchange

PRONUNCIATION

A

The main stress is on the second word, the secondary stress is on the first.

B

1 a **2** a **3** a **4** b **5** b **6** b **7** b

7.3 Reading

READING

B

2

C

1. The writer suggests that Americans are always on the lookout for new ways to live.
2. He or she isn't certain. The odds are against it, but it's possible.
3. Because they were too much like living in a hotel.
4. Because many people like to keep work and home life separate.

D

1 f **2** e **3** c **4** a

7.4 Listening

LISTENING

A

1. Addressing the issue of overcrowding in towns and cities.
2. Because there is no more space for development in urban areas.

B

1. Housing an underground farm
2. Creating an artificial climate
3. Repurposing an industrial facility
4. Keeping things safe and secure
5. Solving a transportation issue

C

1. London
2. tunnels
3. vegetables; herbs
4. water; energy
5. mine
6. commercial
7. energy bills
8. Amsterdam
9. train stations
10. theft

7.5 Write a formal letter of complaint

WRITING

A

1. To complain about a proposal to close/demolish the local library.
2. A member of the local council.
3. The greeting and the sign-off; the language used (e.g. I am writing to you with *regard to* ...); the way it is organized.

B

1 b **2** c **3** a

C

1 b **2** e **3** c **4** a **5** d

WRITING PRACTICE

C

Model answer

Dear Sir/Madam,

I am writing to you to complain about the amount of graffiti in the town center, which gets worse by the day, and what seems to me the lack of any attempt to do anything about it.

I'm sorry, but I feel the authorities are failing in their duty here. Graffiti is a lot like litter and makes the area look shabby and uncared for. I understand the council has actually endorsed the painting of murals on some buildings and I admit some of these add color to the area. But most graffiti is just scrawling by people who want attention or gang members marking out territory. I appreciate that it is expensive to remove graffiti and difficult to keep up with more being written every day. However, I'm afraid that whatever preventative measures you currently have, they are not working. May I suggest larger fines for those caught painting graffiti and a larger number of police officers on the streets?

I feel that more action should be taken on this issue, and I hope that my suggestions will be listened to. I am not alone in thinking that this unattractive practice on our streets should stop. I look forward to hearing what your intentions and plans are in regard to this matter.

Sincerely,

Harriett Pugh

8.1 Myths and legends

GRAMMAR

A

1. must have crashed
2. may/might/could have gotten
3. must have run out
4. may/might/could have been captured
5. may/might/could have reached
6. may/might/could have been found
7. may/might/could have been
8. can't have been

B

1 may/might/could have gotten lost
2 can't /couldn't have stolen the money
3 package must have arrived
4 plane may/might/could have been delayed
5 can't have been born in 1976
6 car must have been stolen
7 can't/couldn't have been Stephen that you saw
8 may/might/could have been French

VOCABULARY

A

1 traditional 2 traditionally 3 believe 4 belief
5 essentially 6 myth 7 mythical 8 legend
9 legendarily 10 resemble 11 represent 12 representative

B

1 mythical 2 Legend 3 resembles 4 traditionally
5 represented 6 believe 7 myth 8 essentially

PRONUNCIATION

A

In Irish folklore, / Cúchulainn is a mythological hero / who appears in many stories. / According to the stories, / during battles, / he is transformed into some kind of monster. / Although descriptions of him differ in the various stories, / most agree that he is extremely handsome. / The stories about Cúchulainn / bear some similarity to other legends from different parts of the world, / most notably / ancient Greece and Persia. /

B

Cúchulainn's most heroic deed was performed at the Raid of Cooley. / Legend has it, / the Irish hero defended Ulster from attack from the men of Connaught. / The leader of Connaught, / Queen Medb, / wanted to conquer Ulster so she could take possession of a magical brown bull / which was owned by the elder warriors of Ulster. /
At the time of the attack, / the men of Ulster were suffering from a bizarre weakness / imposed on them by the goddess Macha. / None of the warriors were able to defend their city. / Cúchulainn, / however, / was unaffected by Macha's curse as he was not merely human – / he was the son of a god. / Cúchulainn went to battle against the whole army of Connaught, / helped only by his father, / the god of light, / and by Morrigan, / the goddess of war. / During the defense, / Cúchulainn is severely wounded, / but his father helps heal his wounds. / He regains his energy / and kills hundreds of Connaught soldiers, / using their dead bodies to build a wall to help defend Ulster. / Eventually, / the men of Ulster regain strength and launch into battle, / forcing their enemy to retreat. /

8.2 Who did it?

VOCABULARY

A

1 listened
2 heard
3 hearing
4 looking
5 felt
6 watching
7 saw
8 looked
9 touched
10 looked

B

1 a 2 f 3 b 4 e 5 d 6 c

C

1 punishment
2 sentenced
3 witnesses
4 investigating
5 accused
6 caught; charged
7 commit
8 innocent
9 proof
10 questioned

GRAMMAR

A

1 We watched an interesting Japanese documentary on Netflix last night.
2 She was wearing a striped cotton shirt she bought on sale.
3 They live in a fantastic old house just outside Charleston.
4 The antique wooden clock struck midnight as he tiptoed down the stairs.
5 Overall, I'd say that it's quite an economical little car.
6 Apparently, she's found a beautiful Italian dress she likes.
7 As I stood up, a small round object on the grass caught my eye.
8 Every day, he ate two large sugar-coated doughnuts for breakfast.
9 The $20 million development includes two large state-of-the-art lecture theaters.
10 The couple found the 16th-century Chinese vase in their backyard.

B

1 It's a charming little coastal town on Cape Cod.
2 correct
3 I bought a new designer suit for my interview.
4 correct
5 correct
6 We live on a long, pleasant tree-lined street in the suburbs.
7 correct
8 We were struck by the beautiful snow-covered hills.

PRONUNCIATION

A

fall-rising

8.3 Reading

READING

C

1 T
2 T

3 F ('… there were supplies of food and water …')
4 F ('Others suggest the ship might have been attacked by pirates, not as improbable as the other theories, but it's unlikely to have been the reason …')
5 T
6 NG (Although both are mentioned as being faulty or broken, there is nothing in the article to suggest the cause of this.)

D

1 To a bottle that had been thrown into the sea.
2 To suggest that no one was in control of the boat.
3 That the papers, like wedding confetti, had been thrown around in a random fashion.

8.4 Listening

LISTENING

C

1 Sales are at their highest ever
2 The basic structure of a crime novel
3 Excitement keeps you entertained
4 Creating an ideal moral world
5 Bringing order to chaos

D

1 c 2 a 3 c 4 b 5 b

8.5 Write a complex essay

WRITING

A

1 The possible causes of the rise in cybercrime and what can be done about it.
2 cybercrime.

B

1 c 2 b

C

2 Conclusion 1 doesn't cover all of the main arguments in the essay and introduces new ideas ('We rely on the authorities to deal with the problem …').

WRITING PRACTICE

C

Model answer

Cyberbullying is among the principal dangers facing young people today, with one in five teenagers saying they have experienced it. This essay will first look at some of the reasons it has become so widespread and the harm it does and will then suggest ways of improving the situation.

The foremost problem is that most teenagers have cell phones, tablets or computers, and most cyber bullying takes place through social media. The result can be serious psychological damage. The main issue facing those wishing to prevent it is that the bully can easily remain anonymous. As a result, parents and teachers can neither see nor hear it. With electronic media, victims can be bullied 24 hours a day wherever they are, and most information communicated electronically is public and permanent.

The fact that cyberbullying is hidden from parents and teachers poses a challenge. One solution is for parents and teachers to better understand the technology and networks their children use. Teachers should be trained to notice changes in behavior that might be a clue to someone being bullied. Another way to tackle the problem is to encourage students to report any abusive messages immediately. In addition, all schools should have counselors to help the victims of bullying to cope with the situation. Another solution might be for tech companies to develop software that blocks offensive or hurtful texts or pictures.

In conclusion, the fact that most young people now have cell phones and computers and are active on social media, and the fact that bullies can remain anonymous, makes it easy for cyberbullies to act undetected. Solving the problem requires the combined effort of parents, teachers, tech companies and, above all, the young people themselves.

9.1 Customers

GRAMMAR

A

1 which
2 that
3 that
4 in which
5 where
6 who
7 that
8 when
9 whose
10 –
11 which
12 –

B

1 We watched a documentary last night which/that was terrible.
2 Could you pass me that book on the table?
3 The first stop on our journey was Ljubljana, which is the capital of Slovenia.
4 My friend just started dating a guy (who/that) I used to work with.
5 Hey, that's the man who/that stole my purse!

C

1 The employee **who/that** dealt with me in the store was really helpful.
2 Online sales, ~~that~~ **which** have increased dramatically over the last year, could be our main source of income soon.
3 We haven't been back to the restaurant ~~when~~ **where** we ate that bad shrimp.
4 I don't know ~~whose~~ **who is** to blame for the poor promotional campaign.
5 correct
6 correct
7 I've no time for managers who**se** sole focus is maximizing profit.
8 Not one of the employees ~~in which~~ **that**/(–) he hired had the right attributes – I'd seriously question his recruitment process.

PRONUNCIATION

A

step down

VOCABULARY

A

1 to
2 about
3 with
4 for
5 about
6 to
7 on
8 for

B

1 argue about
2 consent to
3 deal with
4 insist on
5 adhere to
6 complaining about
7 thank you for
8 apologize for

9.2 Products

VOCABULARY

A

1 theory
2 Researchers
3 findings
4 evidence
5 data
6 analysis

B

1 c 2 a 3 a 4 b 5 b 6 c 7 a 8 c

GRAMMAR

A

1 b 2 f 3 a 4 e 5 d 6 c

B

1 both
2 few
3 either
4 plenty of
5 none
6 Every
7 no
8 any

PRONUNCIATION

A

1 A few‿of
2 A large number‿of
3 a great deal‿of
4 Plenty‿of; none‿of them
5 Some‿of; most‿of them
6 both‿of them; neither‿of them

B

1 Thousands‿of people were sold faulty goods, but only half‿of them complained.
2 There are a whole bunch‿of reasons why I don't trust the brand – lack‿of quality being one of them.
3 Some‿of the best technology on sale these days is manufactured in China.
4 Most‿of the stores on Main Street have survived the recession.
5 A number‿of residents are worried the redevelopment will cause a great deal‿of disruption.

9.3 Reading

READING

B

1 c 2 d 3 a 4 e 5 b

C

1 increased sales/profits ('The first is obviously bigger sales and higher profits.'); publicizing their products ('… companies need to let people know that they have something exciting to offer …'); keeping existing customers ('… businesses have to keep reminding [existing customers] of the satisfaction they received from products in the past.'); attracting new ones ('It's also vital for companies to attract new customers …')
2 Because they might find a newer version of the same product or see a more appealing advertisement ('For existing customers, who might be tempted to switch brands because their rivals have produced a newer version or a more impressive ad …').
3 Today's consumers are not so easy to fool or impress ('Advertisers have also had to adapt to an increasingly knowledgeable audience, who is less easily fooled or impressed.').
4 They made new and more creative ads and became very important ('… presented the public with artsy ads, funny ads or just plain weird ads. This explosion of "creativity" occurred in the 1980s and admen were as much a feature of the cultural landscape as writers, artists and movie stars.').
5 recording ('They are far more likely to record their favorite shows …'); downloading ('… or alternatively download …'); live-streaming ('… or live-stream ad-free content.').
6 It keeps their brand in consumer's minds ('Whether the reaction is positive or negative … then it keeps the brand in consumers' minds.').

9.4 Listening

LISTENING

B

Conversation 1: The woman booked a racquetball court, but arrived late so it has been given to another customer.
Conversation 2: Logan didn't follow his boss's instructions properly and photocopied too many pages, missed a spelling mistake and sealed the envelopes.

C

1 a 2 c 3 a 4 a 5 a 6 b 7 c 8 a

9.5 Write a proposal

WRITING

A

1 The recreation center is losing members due to the negative comments on its website.
2 Changes that could be made in response to the complaints.

B

1 d 2 c 3 a 4 b

C

1 Additionally 2 As a result 3 Furthermore 4 however
5 After all 6 Also 7 Moreover

WRITING PRACTICE

C

Model answer

Introduction

The goal of this proposal is to examine the reasons for poor sales performance and suggest possible changes and improvements that could be made.

Current situation

The main reason sales have been falling year after year is that more people are shopping online. This is part of a general trend in shopping habits and is affecting many retailers on the Main Street. Additionally, criticism has been expressed about our clothing line, claiming that it caters mainly to the middle-aged. Consequently, we fail to attract younger shoppers, the largest demographic for clothes shopping. Although we do provide social amenities for customers, such as a café, we have had suggestions from some customers that we should do more in this area. Specifically, parents shopping with their children voiced this complaint.

Suggestions

One measure we could take is to upgrade our own online presence, establishing a website that provides guided tours of the store and shows what is available and in what sizes and colors. Furthermore, to encourage on-site shopping, we could take measures to make shopping a more pleasant experience by providing in-store entertainment and play areas for children. This would also address the criticism from parents. Finally, hiring a fashion consultant could help to make the stock in our clothing department more attractive to younger buyers.

Final recommendations

Implementation of the ideas suggested above would lead to an increase in the number of customers in store and therefore our profit margin.

10.1 Reporting the news

GRAMMAR

A

Suggested answers

1 if/whether I could turn the TV news off because it was so depressing
2 (that) her cousin works as a journalist for the local paper
3 (that) they couldn't make it because they would be working then
4 (that) he'd been lying to us the whole time
5 (that) the restaurant had gone downhill
6 (that) she'd seen the documentary the previous week
7 if/whether I'd always been interested in current affairs
8 (that) she really had to go because she had work the next day

B

… I asked her how ~~did~~ she ~~get~~ **got** into acting; … she said that she ~~hasn't~~ **hadn't** thought about …; She told me that she ~~was~~ **had been** working as a waitress …; … she told **me** that her mom had persuaded her …; She said that they'd been ~~attending~~ **attended** by none other than …'; … she'd been the most promising actress that she ~~came~~ **had come** across …; She told me that she ~~stops~~ **has stopped** speaking to Von Danke …

VOCABULARY

A

1 tabloids
2 biased
3 headlines
4 newspapers
5 coverage
6 editor
7 subjective
8 sources

B

1 tabloid
2 source
3 editor
4 Broadsheets
5 biased
6 coverage
7 headlines

PRONUNCIATION

A

Rise-fall-rise is used on the first underlined word in each sentence to show the speaker hasn't finished. A fall tone is used at the end to show that they have.

10.2 Digital media

GRAMMAR

A

1 informed
2 convinced
3 explained
4 decided
5 apologized
6 promised

B

1 b 2 a 3 b 4 b 5 a 6 c 7 b 8 a

VOCABULARY

A

1 influencer
2 viral; key factor
3 campaign
4 hashtag
5 to reach; wider audience
6 trending
7 followers
8 meme

B

1 donations
2 audience
3 engagement
4 factor
5 content
6 mentions
7 reaction
8 audience

PRONUNCIATION

A

1 a 2 b 3 a 4 a 5 a 6 b

10.3 Reading

READING

B

1 It was a focal point for the family (the writer describes it as the heart of the living room).
2 Similar to the number of weekly listeners.
3 That both are thought to be no longer used/popular.
4 By being made available online.
5 Its feeling of intimacy; the sense that it is a reliable source of information; the fact that it's often live; its interactivity; the fact that it has a local, national and international reach.

C

1 c 2 e 3 a 4 b 5 d

10.4 Listening

LISTENING

B

She isn't human – she's computer-generated.

C

1 c 2 c 3 b 4 b 5 c

D

1 F (She has 1.5 million followers on Instagram.)
2 T
3 F (The speaker says the story was 'picked up by traditional news outlets'.)
4 T
5 T

10.5 Write a persuasive essay

WRITING

A

1 The views of those who prefer e-books and the views of those who prefer conventional, print books.
2 Give your opinion.

B

c

C

1 paraphrasing the essay question
2 outlining the advantages of e-readers
3 outlining the disadvantages of e-readers
4 giving a personal opinion

D

1 Although
2 However
3 As much as
4 nevertheless
5 while

WRITING PRACTICE

C

Model answer

This question and discussion comes up in almost every generation. The fact that the young invent new ways of communicating which exclude their parents' generation is the way things have always been. And while some people may find the new means of communication confusing, I don't think the language itself is in danger.

Some people argue that young people today don't have an adequate grasp of the rules of grammar, spelling and so on. Samuel Johnson made the same complaint in the 18th century. If it can be shown that this lack is also apparent in other areas, such as school work or formal writing, then there is perhaps cause for concern. Throughout society, there is now a less formal approach to almost all aspects of life, and this is reflected in the language. Furthermore, we all use different languages in different situations. Communicating with friends is not the same as writing an essay or a formal letter.

Changes and additions to the language can be an improvement and open up new possibilities. While I reserve judgement about emojis, communications written using all the resources of digital media, coupled with an active imagination, can be very expressive and entertaining. The language is appropriate to the context.

In short, I am not convinced that a knowledge of the 'correct' use of the language is being lost. On the contrary, language is being adapted to suit both new media and new social contexts.

Notes

Notes

Notes